The Treatment of
Families in Crisis

Donald G. Langsley, M.D.

AND

David M. Kaplan, Ph.D.

With the Collaboration of

FRANK S. PITTMAN III, M.D.

PAVEL MACHOTKA, PH.D.

KALMAN FLOMENHAFT, M.S.W., A.C.S.W.

CAROL D. DEYOUNG, R.N., M.S.

Foreword by ROBERT H. FELIX, M.D.

GRUNE & STRATTON • NEW YORK • LONDON

Grune & Stratton, Inc.
111 Fifth Avenue
New York, New York 10003

Library of Congress Catalog Card Number 68-29400
International Standard Book Number 0-8089-0251-2

Printed in the United States of America

Authors

Donald G. Langsley, M.D.: Professor and Chairman, Department of Psychiatry, University of California School of Medicine, Davis, California. Formerly Associate Professor of Psychiatry, University of Colorado School of Medicine and Director of Inpatient Service, Colorado Psychiatric Hospital, Denver, Colorado.

and

David M. Kaplan, Ph.D: Associate Professor and Director, Division of Clinical Social Work, Stanford University School of Medicine, Palo Alto, California. Formerly Associate Professor and Director of Psychiatric Social Work, University of Colorado School of Medicine, Denver, Colorado.

with the collaboration of

Frank S. Pittman, III, M.D.: Director of Psychiatric Services, Grady Memorial Hospital and Assistant Professor of Psychiatry, Emory University School of Medicine, Atlanta, Georgia. Formerly Staff Psychiatrist, Family Treatment Unit, and Assistant Professor of Psychiatry, University of Colorado School of Medicine, Denver, Colorado.

Pavel Machotka, Ph.D.: Research Psychologist, Family Treatment Unit, and Assistant Professor of Clinical Psychology, University of Colorado School of Medicine, Denver, Colorado.

Kalman Flomenhaft, M.S.W., A.C.S.W.: Research Psychiatric Social Worker, Family Treatment Unit, University of Colorado Medical Center, Denver, Colorado.

Carol D. DeYoung, R.N., M.S.: Associate Director of Nursing, Tri-County District Health Department, Aurora, Colorado. Formerly Psychiatric-Public Health Nurse, Family Treatment Unit, University of Colorado Medical Center, Denver, Colorado.

Contents

This Book is Dedicated

To Our Families

"*I am convinced that if we apply our medical knowledge
and social insights fully, all but a small portion of the
mentally ill can eventually achieve a wholesome and
constructive adjustment. If we launch a broad new
mental health program now . . . many more mentally
ill can be helped to remain in their own homes without
hardship to themselves or their families. Those who
are hospitalized can be helped to return to their own
communities. All but a small proportion can be restored to useful life. We can spare them and their
families much of the misery which mental illness now
entails. We can save public funds and we can conserve
our manpower resources.*"

JOHN F. KENNEDY*

* Message from the President of the United States Relative to Mental Illness
and Mental Retardation. U.S. Government Printing Office, Washington, D.C.,
1963.

Acknowledgments

In a project of this magnitude and time, many have participated whose aid and encouragement should be acknowledged. We will name a few, realizing that it is impossible to list each individual who has contributed in a major way to the Family Treatment Unit. Unfortunately, the limitations of space will not permit the listing of most of the individual Psychiatric Residents and other staff members of the Inpatient Service of Colorado Psychopathic Hospital, the Emergency Psychiatric Service of the University of Colorado Medical Center, and many other individuals on the staff of the University of Colorado School of Medicine and of Colorado General Hospital. Their numbers are many and their aid was immense.

We would like to acknowledge our thanks to a few specific individuals who have been of very special aid. Herbert S. Gaskill, M.D. as Professor and Chairman of the Department of Psychiatry and Director of all clinical psychiatric facilities, offered encouragement and support for the project from its first proposals. Drs. Allen Hodges and Bernard Bloom of the U.S.P.H.S. Regional Office in Denver were of special help in the planning phases of the project. Their consultative skills helped us avoid many pitfalls in the research design. Jay Haley and Drs. Alfred Messer and Andrew Ferber were of great help at many phases of the project. We have continued to rely on them for consultation and encouragement. They are but three of the leaders in the new field of family therapy who have provided consistent interest and stimulation.

Almost twenty-five clinical social workers who have had no other connection with the Project have served as independent raters of the results of the Family Crisis Treatment (for the experimentals) and the Psychiatric Hospital Treatment (for the controls). We promise to list them individually in our final report, but cannot avoid mentioning their help with the evaluative aspects of the Project.

Drs. Kenneth Ash, Harold Chandler, Peter Mayerson, and Glenn Swank were very helpful in their participation in the clinical aspects of the work.

A number of research technicians and secretaries have worked with us loyally and helpfully. We specifically would like to mention the following with our thanks.

Mrs. Mary Neasham	Miss Geraldine Winograd
Mrs. Lorraine Huard	Miss Sylvia Marx
Mrs. Irma Schurman	Mrs. Cheryl Sayers
Mr. William F. Finzer, Jr.	Mrs. Gail Thompson
Mr. James Hoffmeister	Mrs. Catherine DeMatte

In addition, Miss Elaine Steffen has patiently typed many drafts and redrafts of this manuscript and we could not have completed it without her help and that of Mrs. Mary Neasham.

We wish to thank the publisher and his staff for their assistance in preparing the manuscript for publication.

And, of course, the National Institute of Mental Health! Not just for their five year financial support (Grant Number MH 1577) which made it possible to do this demonstration and evaluation project, but for the interest and encouragement in providing crisis therapy, family therapy, and community psychiatric services for all citizens. The years ahead will surely validate the wisdom and foresight of the Joint Commission and Dr. Robert H. Felix in planning for comprehensive psychiatric services and that of the staffs of N.I.M.H. in helping this movement grow.

THE AUTHORS

Foreword

In 1965, I was afforded the opportunity to review the history of care for the mentally ill and the prospects for the future.* At that time this nation had enacted legislation to encourage the establishment of mental health services for all citizens. The dreams were initiated by the work of the Joint Commission on Mental Illness and Health and by legislation encouraged by President Kennedy and enacted by the 88th Congress. The United States had reached the point where the concept of and know how for treatment of mental illnesses had progressed beyond institutionalization with the resulting removal of the sufferers from their families, communities and usual occupations. Adding to the humane considerations of the Dorothea Dix era, science had developed treatments which aided the recovery and rehabilitation of the seriously mentally ill. The development of the psychoactive drugs permitted locked wards to be opened and patients to be treated near their homes. Increased numbers of patients formerly sent to a mental hospital were being treated in settings such as general hospitals. Outpatient clinics and agencies were increasing the facilities which the community required to provide the optimum in treatment whether this be in or out of hospital.

The model of the comprehensive community mental health center was elaborated only a few years ago. It included diagnostic and treatment functions, follow-up and rehabilitative services, consultation, public education, community research and prevention. Having had some role in the development and application of that model, it has been gratifying to witness its growth. A significant number of such centers have been established in urban, suburban, and rural areas. There has been considerable experimentation in developing services and centers appropriate to local conditions. Partially as a result of the availability of community treatment, state hospital populations are decreasing visibly, and we can view with pride the success these centers have had in prevention, treatment and rehabilitation.

The mental health demonstration project reported in this book by Doctors Langsley and Kaplan and their colleagues, is an example of the community mental health philosophy which seeks to avoid unnecessary hospitalization, which seeks to keep patients

functioning in their usual roles and which focuses on the family as
a source of strength as well as an arena of problems. It originates
from the hospital where I had my own psychiatric training, which
I knew as the Colorado Psychopathic Hospital, now renamed
"Psychiatric." Even as long ago as when I was a trainee in that
center, our faculty was teaching us to look to the modern mental
hospital as the facility for treatment as opposed to custody. While
it is a source of personal pleasure to see that hospital and the
University of Colorado continue its willingness to try new models
and test new approaches, it is in their tradition and what I have
come to expect of my alma mater. It is encouraging to see that the
originators of this project carefully built in a design which would
compare family crisis therapy with a control group and which uses
baseline and follow-up measures to test the results. It is all too easy
to report enthusiasm when one tries new approaches, but hard data
studies are all too few. The authors have been aware that other
experimental programs in mental health services have avoided
admission to a psychiatric hospital but, not satisfied to report only
their success in keeping patients out of the hospital, Langsley and
Kaplan have studied the post-treatment adjustment of each patient
as well. They have been conservative in interpreting their results
and have been alert to sources of error in drawing their conclusions.

The family crisis therapy described here is one demonstration
that, in a high proportion of cases, immediate care can avoid
regression and decompensation. It is convincing evidence that
avoiding admission to a mental hospital removes the patient from
a path towards chronicity. This approach focuses on the fact that
mental hospitals have all too often been used, not so much as a
therapeutic tool, as a facility which makes possible the removal
of a troubled (and troublesome) individual from the community.
The centuries-old practice of ascribing mental illness to super-
natural forces and sin and society's fear of the man bereft of his
reason led to the "alienation" concept and the removal of the
psychiatric patient from his community. It is hard enough to change
old ways of thinking, but harder still radically to alter time-honored
behavior which proceeded from that thinking. By seeing the whole
family and by explicitly making clear the view that the problem
can be dealt with by the family, this approach becomes family
centered and returns to the family doctor who espouses the principle that the community is concerned about and will care for its own.
Just as the family physician is often the first contact point for his

patients (families) when they need medical care or advice, family treatment through him offers similar immediate support.

The experiments reported in this book also recognize an economic reality. We are not a country with infinite resources, and we are obliged to conserve our assets. Among these assets are the productivity of the hospitalizable patient which is lost during hospitalization. The ability to keep our citizens working in their usual jobs (in industry, managing a household or raising the next generation) conserves our resources. A human being deprived of earning his own way is in danger of losing his self-esteem, and this is always a danger in prolonged hospitalization. The difference in cost between family crisis therapy and mental hospital treatment is another factor of significant importance in planning mental health services for our citizens. The authors have demonstrated that brief but immediately available treatment will keep many patients out of hospital. They are now engaged in comparing the results of their treatment with a similar group of hospitalized patients at six and eighteen months after the end of treatment. They tell us that their results are encouraging and the preliminary data which they do present are indeed suggestive. If their estimates are correct that family crisis therapy can be made available for approximately one sixth the cost of mental hospital treatment, this would have very significant implications for planning mental health services.

I have said elsewhere that "professionals and the general public alike have been moving with increasing enthusiasm and speed toward more rational and practical concepts of mental illnesses and methods, not only for overcoming but for preventing them."* This approach to family crises is a form of secondary prevention—early case finding and prompt treatment. If it teaches families to deal with crises without seeking admission to a mental hospital, its possibilities for even greater prevention are further extended.

ROBERT H. FELIX, M.D.
Dean
St. Louis University
  School of Medicine
Formerly Director,
National Institute of
  Mental Health

* Felix, Robert H.: *Mental Illness: Progress and Prospects.* #16, Bampton Lectures in America (1965). New York, Columbia University Press, 1967.

Introduction

This book describes technics for treating families in crisis. It reports on a project at Colorado Psychopathic* Hospital in Denver established to test whether family crisis therapy could provide an effective alternative to psychiatric hospitalization. The basic principles of family crisis therapy are not new. They have been utilized in the treatment of individuals and families in various kinds of crises. To the best of our knowledge, however, this project is the first to test crisis treatment for whole families which include a person who would ordinarily be admitted to a mental hospital. It seems reasonable to assume that the principles of treating families at times of crisis would be equally applicable to less serious crises among more healthy populations. It is hoped that this book will be of interest to those to whom individuals and families come for help in times of crisis. In addition to the mental health professions (psychiatry, psychology, social work, and nursing), this includes family physicians, teachers, ministers, and other counsellors and helpers.

Until very recently, the psychiatric hospital was thought of as the very best and primary resource for the acutely disturbed patient. In the last two hundred years, the mental hospital has shown wide variations in its effectiveness as a treatment setting.[6] But as the movement for community care of the mentally ill has gathered momentum, the role of the mental hospital as a treatment and rehabilitative agency has been scrutinized increasingly and often critically.

The case against the custodial mental hospital has been well documented.[14,19] Custodial care means abandoning patients to progressive deterioration (which is not a result of disease but rather of institutionalization) and to social breakdown in subsequent functioning.[13] Those few patients who are released from such hospitals months or years later have a difficult time finding a place in a society which did not expect them back. The family has

---

*Renamed Colorado Psychiatric Hospital, July 1, 1967.

xv

closed ranks during the absence and reorganized itself to function without the patient.[4]

What about the psychiatric hospital that offers treatment rather than custody? How effective is such a setting for the subsequent adjustment of the patient in the community? Here again, we have considerable evidence to indicate that when the mental hospital is organized to offer long-term treatment, the post-hospital adjustment is disappointing. These patients are characterized by high functional disability, are poor rehabilitative bets and have high readmission rates.[9,16,25] Their families still tend to close ranks during their treatment in the hospital and to deal with the ex-patient by rehospitalization when subsequent stresses exert themselves. The patient himself tends to run back to the hospital.

If we examine the record of the mental hospital which offers brief treatment and compare its results with the long-term treatment setting, there is less disability, better rehabilitative outlook, better post-hospital functioning and some indication that these patients can remain longer in the community following hospitalization.[16,19,25,30] But the negative effects of mental hospitalization persist, particularly repeated hospitalizations.

Evaluative studies have determined that the shorter the hospital stay, the better the post-discharge functioning.[9,16] An important issue which needs to be considered is the effect of psychiatric hospitalization, irrespective of duration. If social disability is reduced by shorter hospitalization, avoiding hospitalization altogether is the best way of preventing social breakdown.[14]

There is much to suggest that it is a devastating experience for families to live with a member labeled "crazy." The label "mental patient" is largely a result of admission to a psychiatric hospital. It has been suggested that the public's well documented fear and reaction to "mental patients" is based not on behavior and symptoms, but on the label itself. In a survey, most people were unperturbed by descriptions of the most serious psychoses but they wouldn't want a mental hospital dischargee with or without symptoms living next door.[4] Statistics do not convey the anguish, the shame, or the fear that families experience, nor do numbers reflect the disruption, conflict, isolation, and the enormous amount of energy spent in trying to live with and deny the stigma associated with mental illness.[17,20] The picture has been best portrayed by novelists and playwrights. Typically, those families who live with someone who has been labeled mentally ill fear the harm that the patient may inflict upon himself or on others. They worry about progressive deterioration of the patient and all the extra care and responsibility he requires. They live with the suspicion that others in the family may be similarly affected and with the fear that their children may inherit a similar disorder. While families vary in their reactions, some measure of isolation, restriction, and recrimination creeps into family living. A greater sensitivity and avoidance of everyday stress occurs in the belief that these pressures may aggravate the patient and cause a resurgence of his illness. Members of such families experience a weakening of the family's ability to mediate stress for its members and a heightened tendency to scapegoat the patient or to exclude him by hospitalization rather than attempting to cope with the usual crises of living.

So much of the family's energy goes into fear, worry, hiding, and denying or protecting themselves against the fears of insanity that a good deal of the joy of living and the ability to function are seriously blunted.[27] The contribution of these families to the community is necessarily limited. They typically require larger measures of community resources in order to function, even at lower levels.

The popular conception of insanity is that of a terrifying, mysterious illness. It is identified with suicide, assaultive, and bizarre behavior, with chronic progressive disability and with inherited transmission. This view of mental illness is highly exaggerated and sterotyped; nevertheless, this conception is widely held. Unfortunately it encourages and elicits from the sick member the very behavior that is most feared.

The label "mental patient" is largely a result of the act of placing a patient in a psychiatric hospital.[4] Much can be gained by not labeling the patient as "crazy." These patients can receive the protection and treatment they need without acquring such a label. They can receive the help they need without being admitted to a mental hospital.

For those who would continue to make extensive use of psychiatric hospitalization, the question should be posed: "What does mental hospitalization accomplish?" It is increasingly clear that brief hospitalization is becoming the dominant mode of treatment in the mental hospital. Brief psychiatric hospitalization can hope to accomplish: (1) recompensation and remission of symptoms in the patient, (2) the protection of the patient and others during periods of crisis and exacerbation, (3) the provision of a period of rest for the patient and family when they have reached the point of exhaustion, frustration, and confusion. This period of hospitalization can be used to allow patient and family to sort out what has been going on and to permit all participants to renew their energies so that the problems of living can be taken up again by the family and patient.

But evaluative studies suggest that the type of treatment offered during hospitalization has little or no bearing on the post-hospital adjustment of the patient. To expect results which go beyond recompensation may be largely illusory.[16,31] Are these results of brief psychiatric hospitalization worth the risks and cost? The answer is negative if there are effective alternatives. The evidence available suggests that these benefits of mental hospitalization can be achieved by other means.[11,22] A very large proportion of patients currently being hospitalized can be recompensated by emergency outpatient care.[2,23] Hospitalization today is much too readily available; alternative care is not. As a consequence, psychiatric hospitalization is a much abused resource. The relatively small numbers of patients who do require hospitalization could receive treatment in general hospitals and mental health centers close to home, an avenue of treatment strongly recommended by the Joint Commission report.

There are other compelling reasons for treating as many disturbed patients as possible in outpatient programs. Requests for mental hospitalization are not simply a function of the patient's illness. These requests are affected by a variety of social factors including: (1) productivity and usefulness of the patient in his family and community, (2) the family and community's tolerance of the patient's behavior, (3) the extent to which the patient is visible as a deviant member of society, (4) the resources available, which vary from community to community over time, (5) the need of society for marginally productive members (e.g., during wartime the need for production alters society's tolerance for the marginally productive group).

There have been a number of epidemiologic studies which indicate that as many "patients" remain in the community as are hospitalized.[22,28] Those families which request hospitalization for a member, often do so because they have not been able to resolve the stresses which impinge on them.[29] Requests for mental hospitalization are typically based on a sense of panic and frustration. The family comes to believe that it can no longer manage on its own when in fact, many of these families with outpatient help can continue to live with a member who becomes disturbed.[27,30] Scapegoating one member who is perceived as the source of difficulty in the family permits the others to avoid their part in unresolved problems. Querido points out that removing a family member to a psychiatric hospital obscures the interpersonal issues which precipitate his decompensation.[23] Hospitalization offers the patient and family a reward for running away from problems which need to be dealt with. Family requests for psychiatric hospitalization should be regarded as evidence of a disequilibrium within the system of the family. With such an orientation, it is possible to give the patient and family the help they require to avoid removing the designated patient from the family and community.

The present upsurge of interest in outpatient emergency treatment is an outgrowth of the community mental health movement and is based in part on awareness of the inadequacy of the mental hospital as a primary treatment resource as well as the growing conviction that community care is more useful.[1,3,12,24] In the past, emergency treatment programs have developed in relation to some temporary but pressing community need. During wartime for example, large numbers of soldiers were lost to military duty when psychiatric care was provided in hospitals distant from the front lines.[8] Military psychiatry has been reorganized to prevent casualties associated with removal from the soldier's primary unit. Following World War II, an emergency program was instituted in Amsterdam as a result of the lack of hospital beds which were bombed out. The home treatment program was highly effective in reducing the numbers of patients admitted to mental hospitals.[23] But until recently, little use was made of these experiences in the development and improvement of community outpatient emergency psychiatric services.[15,18,26]

A number of demonstrations in this country and abroad have shown that many psychiatric hospitalizations can be avoided when outpatient emergency services are available.[2,11,21,22] While there is little systematic study of what happens to those patients whose hospitalization is unnecessary, there is some indication that their subsequent adjustment is as good or better than those of similar groups who have been hospitalized.[22]

A number of questions have been raised about outpatient programs which attempt to avoid psychiatric hospitalization. Some ask whether such treatment merely delays hospitalization. This of course depends on the alternative care program available. The evidence of the Pasamanick study suggests that the treatment of serious mental illness at home can do more than delay; it can, in fact, prevent hospitalization.[22]

Another question is often raised as to the effect of avoiding hospitalization on the family. Is it helpful or harmful to the patient and to others in his family? Some clinicians suggest that keeping patients at home means turning the home into a hospital at great cost in stress on the family. The evidence indicates, however, that patients who avoid hospitalization do as well or better in terms of subsequent instrumental functioning than those hospitalized.[16] Less is known about what it means to families to live with seriously disturbed members. Undoubtedly, there are families that would be "better off" without certain members who contribute little and who manage to seriously disrupt family life. However, the Grad & Sainsbury study indicated greater desire on the part of families to keep their "patients" at home despite the increased problems created thereby.[10]

The past quarter centry has seen increasing public acceptance of and demand for mental health services.[5,7] The federal program of comprehensive community mental health centers has explicated the goal of providing treatment for all those with mental or emotional problems regardless of where they live or of their race, religion, or economic status. The traditional treatments for mental illness have been a polarity of either long-term individual psychotherapy or mental hospitalization. But on the one hand individual psychotherapy is unavailable in sufficient quantity to meet the demand and on the other hand, hospitalization is usually not necessary. In the face of an acute crisis, it has become increasingly apparent that brief treatment can help resolve the problem, prevent further decompensation, chronicity and incapacity from institutionalization, and can free up the individual and his family for more adaptive problem solving. Those who have pioneered in crisis treatment are well aware of its potential for relief of pain and symptoms. They do not pretend that it changes long established patterns of maladaptive or immature behavior. Change of this magnitude requires other approaches to treatment. The authors hope to see expansion and enlargement of emergency psychiatric services throughout this country, not as the only approach to the treatment of mental illness, but as the principal method for treating psychiatric decompensation.

Perhaps an introduction to the Family Treatment Unit itself is in order. During 1963-64 the senior authors (DGL and DMK) were doing pilot clinical work with families which included a patient who had been judged in need of immediate mental hospitalization. Their observation led to a proposal for a mental health demonstration project which was funded as a five year study by the National Institute of Mental Health (Grant #MH-1577). Since June 1964, the Family Treatment Unit has been studying the use of family crisis treatment for a random sample of patients who have appeared in the Emergency Room of CPH requesting hospitalization. All patients who have been evaluated by the psychiatric resident in the Emergency Room and felt to be in need of immediate hospitalization, who live in a family, and who live within an hour's travel of CPH (Adams, Arapahoe, Denver, and Jefferson Counties) constitute the population from which the experimental sample is drawn. Those not randomly selected for family crisis treatment are available as a pool of control cases from which a matched sample is drawn to compare the results of family crisis treatment and mental hospital treatment. Most of the clinical work with families has been done by a fulltime clinical team consisting of Dr. Frank S. Pittman III (Psychiatrist), Mr. Kalman Flomenhaft, M.S.W. (Psychiatric Social Worker), and Miss Carol D. DeYoung, R.N.,M.S. (Psychiatric-Public Health Nurse). Many research activities of the project have been carried on by a Social Psychologist, Dr. Pavel Machotka. The Director and Co-Director of the project (DGL and DMK) have functioned as administrators, consultants, participants in the clinical work, and planners of the research activities. The work has been further supported by secretarial assistants and research technicians and by a group of psychiatric social workers who have functioned as independent raters of experimental and control families.

This is the first of two books. In this volume as we complete our case gathering activities, we offer our clinical technics and experience with 186 families. In another year or two we will have completed the follow-up evaluations of the 186 experimental and 150 control families. We will then be able to offer a systematic evaluation of the results of family crisis therapy and mental hospital treatment. The project design consists of baseline evaluations of both experimentals and controls, plus follow-up evaluations at three months, six months, eighteen months, thirty months, etc. The instruments used include two measures of individual patient functioning, a measure of family crisis and crisis management before and after treatment, a measure of family role delineation and performance together with independent clinical evaluations. To offer impressions on the preliminary data available at this point would be premature. Suffice it to say that the full data on the first portion of both samples gives us every reason to be encouraged and enthusiatic.

In this book the history of crisis theory and treatment will be reviewed in the first chapter. The second chapter will be an outline of the method of family crisis treatment. A third chapter will deal with a potpourri of clinical topics. There will follow four chapters, each of which is a detailed case study illustrating the specific technics utilized. The cases selected have been chosen for their teaching value. They do not represent every conceivable kind of family crisis, but do illustrate various approaches.

The eighth chapter will describe psychologic tests useful in evaluating families and in particular, the design and instruments of the evaluation of this family crisis treatment. Chapter nine will describe the results of family crisis treatment, principally in terms of clinical description, but will include data on the avoidance of hospitalization. A final chapter will offer a summary and conclusions.

It is our hope that these technics will be of use to those who work with families in crisis and in the prevention of unnecessary admissions to mental hospitals.

Bibliography

1. Bellak, Leopold and Small, Leonard. *Emergency Psychotherapy and Brief Psychotherapy.* New York: Grune & Stratton, 1965.

2. Carse, Joshua, Panton, Nydia E., and Watt, Alexander. A district mental health service: The Worthing Experiment. Lancet. January 4, 1958. pp. 39-42.

3. Coleman, M. Donald and Zwerling, Israel. The emergency psychiatric clinic: a flexible way of meeting community mental health needs. Amer. J. Psychiat. 115:980, 1959.

4. Cumming, Elaine and Cumming, John. *Closed Ranks: An Experiment in Mental Health Education.* Cambridge: Harvard University Press, 1957.

5. Fenichel, Otto. *The Psychoanalytic Theory of Neurosis* New York: W. W. Norton, 1945.

6. Freeman, Howard E. and Simmons, Ozzie G. *The Mental Patient Comes Home.* New York; Wiley, 1963.

7. Freud, S. *Beyond The Pleasure Principle* (1920). London: The Hogarth Press, 1961.

8. Glass, Albert J. Psychiatry in the Korean Campaign: a historical review. U.S. Armed Forces Med. J. 4:1563-83, 1953.

9. Goldberg, E. M. Hospital work and family: a four year study of young mental hospital patients. Brit. J. Psychiat. 112:177-96, 1966.

10. Grad, Jacqueline and Sainsbury, Peter. Problems of caring for the mentally ill at home. Proc. Roy. Soc. of Med. 59:20-23, 1966.

11. Greenblatt, Milton et. al. *The Prevention of Hospitalization: Treatment Without Admission for Psychiatric Patients.* New York: Grune & Stratton, 1963.

12. Grinker, Roy R. and Spiegel, John. *Men Under Stress.* Philadelphia: Blakiston, 1945.

13. Gruenberg, Ernest M. The social breakdown syndrome—some origins. Amer. J. Psychiat. 123:1481-89, 1967.

14. Hunt, R. C. Ingredients of a rehabilitation program. In: Boudreau, F. C. and Gruenberg, E. M. (Eds): *Approach to the Prevention of Disability From Chronic Psychoses.* New York: Milbank Memorial Fund, 1958.

15. Kaplan, David M. and Mason, Edward A. Maternal reactions to premature birth viewed as an acute emotional disorder. Amer. J. Orthopsychiat. 30:539-47, 1960.

16. Lehrman, Nathaniel S. Follow-up of brief and prolonged psychiatric hospitalization. Compr. Psychiat. 2:227-40, 1961.

17. Lewis, Verl S. and Zeichner, Abraham M. Impact of admission to a mental hospital on the patients family. Mental Hygiene, 44:503-9, 1960.

18. Lindemann, Erich. Symptomatology and management of acute grief. Amer. J. Psychiat. 101:141-48, 1944.

19. Mendel, Werner M. Effect of length of hospitalization on rate and quality of remission from acute psychotic episodes. J. Nerv. Ment. Dis. 143:226-33, 1966.

20. Miller, Dorothy and Dawson, William H. Effects of stigma on re-employment of ex-mental patients. Ment. Hyg. 49:281-287, 1965.

21. Meyer, Roger E., Schiff, Lawrence F. and Becker, Alvin. The home treatment of psychotic patients: an analysis of 154 cases. Amer. J. Psychiat. 123:1430-38, 1967.

22. Pasamanick, Benjamin, Scarpitti, Frank R. and Dinitz, Simon. *Schizophrenics in the Community:* An Experimental Study in the Prevention of Hospitalization. New York: Appleton-Century-Crofts, 1967.

23. Querido, A. Early diagnosis and treatment services . In: *Elements of a Community Mental Health Program.* New York: Milbank Memorial Fund, 1956.

24. Rosenthal, Hattie R. Emergency Psychotherapy: A crucial need. Psychoanal. Rev. 52:446-59, 1965.

25. Ruesch, Jurgen. Hospitalization and social disability. J. Nerv. Ment. Dis. 142:203-14, 1966.

26. Semrad, Elvin V. and Zaslow, Stephen L. Assisting the psychotic patient to recompensate. Ment. Hosp. 15:361-66, 1964.

27. Smith, Colin M. and Levey, Archibald B. The follow-up study in psychiatry Dis. Nerv. Syst. 27:595-99, 1966.

28. Srole, Leo et al. *Mental Health in the Metropolis: The Manhattan Midtown Study,* Vol. 1. New York: McGraw-Hill, 1962.

29. Vincent, Clark E. Mental health and the family. J. of Marriage and the Family, 29:18-38, 1967.

30. Wood, Edwin C., Rakusin, John M. and Morse, Emanuel. Interpersonal aspects of psychiatric hospitalization: I Admission. Arch. Gen. Psychiat. 3:632-41, 1960.

31. Zubin, J., et. al. Epidemiological aspects of prognosis in mental illness. In: Pasamanick, B. (Ed.): *Epidemiology of Mental Disorder,* Washington, D. C.: A.A.A.S, 1959.

CHAPTER 1

Crisis: A Different Approach
to Mental Illness

During the twentieth century, studies of abnormal human behavior have focused heavily on the psychologic history of the
individual.[10,12,13] Each symptom, each bit of disturbance, is seen
as a repetition of past conflicts. The problems an adult woman has
with men are a replay of her childhood difficulties with her father.
When a young man sings, "I want a girl, just like the girl, that
married dear old dad," he is expressing more than his pleasure in
the tune. The words have real significance, and each young man
finds a mate with the characteristics of his mother. History is constantly repeating itself.

And it is true! We find in all behavior some traces of the past.
Freud's discoveries of transference phenomena, of the timelessness
of the unconscious and of the genetic point of view have influenced
us to focus on today's behavior as being motivated by enduring
intrapsychic conflict. For the past few decades the most valued
treatment for mental disturbances has been intensive individual
psychotherapy.[5] To re-create infantile conflicts in the relationship
with a psychotherapist (in order to make them conscious, differ-
entiate the past from the present, and work out adult solutions)
has been the goal of individual-oriented treatment. This type of
treatment has of necessity avoided the reality problems of the
present and the social field in which the patient lives. The consistent findings of some elements of the past in present-day behavior and of the persistence of intrapsychic structures have kept
much attention focused on the past and too little on the problems of
the present.

Mental health professionals have attended to the problems of
the present only when they led to emergencies.[9] A pressing, but
temporary community need might evoke some action. Interest in

1

military psychiatric emergencies blossoms during times of war and languishes as soon as the military emergency is over.[14,15] When psychiatric hospital beds were unavailable in Amsterdam, home treatment services were developed.[28] Professional interest in such programs seems to last only as long as the need is urgent. Coleman has pointed to the understanding and treatment of psychiatric emergencies (crises) as an "area of silence."[9] The theoretic position which views psychiatric emergencies as exacerbations of chronic disorders promotes this lack of interest in crisis treatment. World War II was the setting for the pioneer work of Grinker and Spiegel but they took the point of view that: "Every war neurosis is a psychoneurosis since the old unsolved conflicts of the past are stimulated by stress to assist in the production of a neurotic reaction . . ."[15]

As long as reactions to trauma are conceived of merely as derivatives of old internal conflicts, one ignores the fact that they may be psychologic phenomena uniquely organized under the stress conditions of the present. The advances in psychoanalytic theory of the ego psychology era have been those which have refused the temptation to be simplistic. The growth of the ego's problem solving capacities have been seen as dependent on the present as well as the past. Hartmann's concept of optimum frustration suggests that an ideal amount of stress is productive of change and growth and that stress is an important part of the explanation for behavior. Erikson's contribution to psychoanalytic theory has been to point to nodal problems which must be solved (crises) before further growth can take place. He views much of that which we call disturbed behavior or psychopathology, as a reaction to the internal crisis and the environment. If the environment is helpful, the problem is worked out and growth continues. If the environment is not helpful, the individual continues to have a problem which stunts his further development and which may produce symptoms or disturbed behavior.

Thus life is a series of crises, large and small, and on their management depends the outcome of growth or regression. Yet surprisingly little attention has been paid to crisis psychology, to the social field in which the crisis occurs and to the treatment of crisis. There is much to suggest that acute upsets are a sign of an ongoing struggle to master a currently disruptive situation. Most of life goes on when an individual is not in crisis, but is meeting his needs. At these times he is described as being "in equilibrium." But the equilibrium is often interrupted by disruptive pressures or stresses, either from within the individual's psychologic self, his biologic processes, or from the milieu in which he lives. These pressures upset the previous balance and the person is said to now be in a state of "crisis." [20,25]

The essence of crisis is struggle—a struggle to master an upsetting situation and to regain a state of balance. The crisis has been defined as the combination of the hazardous events which precipitate an imbalance and the individual's reaction to the events. A crisis precipitated by various hazardous events creates a situation in which the individual cannot cope. Previously successful coping mechanisms are obviously not successful in resolving the problem posed by the current stress and the established ego-adaptive mechanisms become inoperative, accentuating the individual's sense of being overwhelmed.[8,17,18,21,25]

Acute upsets are generally self-correcting. The stresses are usually such as to fall within the range of Hartmann's "optimal frustration" and after a variable, but brief period, the pre-stress coping functions return and with them some sense of control.[16] The mastery of the stress enlarges the individual's ego and his repertoire of solutions to problems. But it does not always work out so well. In some instances the hazardous events put an intolerable amount of stress on the individual. His own problem solving capacities may be inadequate because of the stress, or because of his own personality factors (ego strengths) or because of factors in the current social field in which he lives. All three kinds of forces influence stress outcome.

The struggle to cope with the crisis does not take place in a vacuum, but occurs in the context of the individual's social field. This field includes a variety of social subsystems which influence the struggle for stress mastery.[33] Stress mastery is influenced by relationships with significant other people with whom the individual is in regular contact such as family members, friends, and fellow workers or community caretakers.[22] Querido emphasizes the significance of field factors by pointing out that removing a family member from the community (by putting him in a mental hospital) obscures the interpersonal issues which may have precipitated the decompensation.[28]

Long-term psychotherapy is concerned with intrapsychic problems which have been chronic. Stress intervention deals with an individual engaged in a struggle to cope with a current situation. The past conflicts and personality factors of the given person will influence how the stress manifests itself, but if the current problem can be mastered, the old conflicts assume less importance.

What does this have to do with mental illness and with psychiatric hospitals? It might be argued that the patterns observed in psychotic individuals have been present for years and have nothing to do with acute problems, stresses, and crisis. But psychosis begins with acute stress as the precipitant in most cases. There are many potentially psychotic individuals who are not decompensated, who are not clinically symptomatic. The susceptibility to psychosis and regression is present in the form of a weakened ego which cannot master stress. In the face of a crisis, such susceptible individuals become acutely ill, and show the symptoms of an acute clinical syndrome. Without immediate treatment, the acute illness becomes a chronic one, influenced not only by the patient but also by the form of the treatment. An acute patient placed in a setting which encourages the sick role and which promotes regression and hospitalism will soon become a chronic patient. It is therefore a basic assumption in crisis treatment, that adequate help at the time of the emergency will prevent chronic illness.

The treatment of psychiatric emergencies has been influenced by several treatment models. Each has emphasized one or more aspects of stress mastery described here. Each model has contributed important treatment strategies and technics. The major models will be reviewed briefly to highlight and contrast their unique contributions.

PATIENT-ORIENTED MODELS

Recompensation Model

There are two models which focus exclusively on the patient and which see the crisis as something which happens to a single individual. These two models are the recompensation model and the limited psychotherapy model. The recompensation model of treatment views a crisis as a person falling apart and the treatment as that which is necessary to put him back together again.[30] The focus is on the fact that the patient is falling apart right now. It does not necessarily attempt to go to the past to understand why the patient is falling apart. On the other hand, the limited psychotherapy model assumes that the crisis is related not only to the fact that the patient is falling apart right now but that the recent stress has activated old conflicts.[9] Treatment consists of interpretation and understanding of some of these old conflicts.

In the recompensation model far less attention is paid to the past. Crisis results when a single individual suffers stress and fails to cope with it. The failure to cope is not necessarily explained. What is important is the fact that the individual involved does not adapt but instead falls apart. He decompensates! Whereas his previous level of functioning may have been more or less satisfactory, with the decompensation, he regresses. The person who loses a job, becomes exceedingly upset and unable to effectively get another one, who then proceeds to exhibit psychotic thinking and maladaptive behavior, has decompensated. The reasons for his regression are not specifically sought. Instead, the therapist only wants to halt the decompensation and regression and to return the patient to the pre-stress level of functioning. That pre-stress level may have been less than ideal but the recompensation model does not propose to make the patient healthier and more mature than he was before. It only hopes to get him back to whatever the previous level of functioning happened to be. The pre-stress ego functions that have become temporarily inoperative because of the decompensation are to be restored.

The military treatment model and the traumatic neurosis model are typical examples of the recompensation approach to treatment. In military psychiatry the most frequently seen psychiatric casualty is the individual who is overwhelmed by the intensity of the stress of war. Very simple principles developed in World War II and Korea have been highly effective in getting the soldier put back together and put back to fighting. The treatment is carried out in close proximity to the military unit. This discourages regression whereas to send a soldier far behind the lines into a psychiatric unit far from the front implies that he is expected to be sick for a long while. The treatment consists of a brief period of rest from the overwhelming stimuli in order to collect energy for the task of mastering the trauma. In addition, the military patient is often provided with an opportunity to discharge the suppressed motor phenomena and the emotions experienced during the trauma. This abreaction and catharsis is effective in stress mastery. Of course this does not go into the soldier's background. It does not explain why this particular stress constituted a trauma. The recompensation treatment carries with it the implicit message "pull yourself together and get back to duty." The treatment depends in large part on the nonspecific help associated with rest and a warm meal. To explain it in psychologic terms, one would probably go back to the model of the distressed child being looked after by the concerned parent.

Another example of the operation of the decompensation and its treatment is being used more frequently in general hospital emergency rooms. Kritzer and Pittman have reported on the use of overnight holding beds in the emergency area. Other crisis treatment units are recognizing that a backup unit where a few beds are available for very brief recompensation treatment are helpful (the Fort Logan Crisis Intervention Unit and the Connecticut Mental Health Center). When a patient is admitted to such a unit he may be dramatically delirious or psychotic. The nonspecific help of rest (with or without drugs), food, shelter, and other nonspecific professional care is frequently effective in a short while.

Semrad has written several papers about the treatment of severe decompensated states (psychotic patients in a mental hospital).[30] He made use of the therapeutic relationship over a longer period of time to accomplish the recompensation of the patient. The first phases have to do with reopening and clarifying the patient's relationships and communication lines with other human beings. The treatment focuses on the patient's current reality and is not oriented to the past. Recompensation then proceeds by discussing with the patient the recent precipitating stresses. Using such reality oriented discussions of events reasonably nearby in time, the therapist operates as an active and real person. He helps the patient face and cope with reality once again. This is accomplished principally through the relationship. The goal is to reestablish the previously existing levels of functioning. In reviewing the recent stresses, the purpose is not limited to the solution of those problems that precipitated the decompensation. It is often the goal of the therapist to help the patient do a better job of coping with future stress situations. In order to do this, the patient has to be returned to his prestress level of operation. The supportive relationships with other people that had previously existed must be restored.

The Brief Psychotherapy Model

In individual psychotherapy a high premium is placed on insight. Many clinicians believe that lasting effect occurs only if the patient acquires insight into the repressed genetic antecedent of the current problem. The crisis is seen as a repetition of earlier traumata. Fenichel points out that: "what is most characteristic in the reaction to a trauma is that associative connections are immediately established between the trauma and the infantile conflicts that become activated. Old infantile threats and anxieties suddenly reappear and assume a serious character. The trauma may be experienced as a repetition of older traumata of childhood".[10]

In an extensive psychotherapeutic approach the goals of treatment are to give the patient as much insight in as many areas of the repressed past as possible. The limited psychotherapy model, however, suggests that crises may be dealt with by restricting the breadth but not the depth of the goals. Within the specific area of the trauma the therapist hopes to help the patient achieve insight. The traditional technics of psychotherapy are utilized, including the interpretation of transference and the working through of insights. Coleman describes the goal of this kind of brief psychotherapy as "a minimal restructuring of key conflictual areas in an acutely decompensated personality (designed to) bring the patient back to his previous level of function or halt further decompensation."[9] Bellak defines brief psychotherapy as a treatment utilizing the classic technics of an insight orientation.[4] Interpretation is the effective tool. The therapist hopes to make conscious certain areas from the past which have been repressed.

Coleman emphasizes the importance of support for those activities where defense combines with gratification which is adaptive. He urges that adaptive defenses be strengthened and reinforced. In this manner the therapist hopes to restore the ego's temporarily impaired integrative capacity. This may result in a spontaneous healing process.

In this brief psychotherapy approach the precipitating stress is not necessarily significant as a separate event. It is important because it triggers an earlier conflict and the combination of the current event (the stress) plus the susceptibility of a patient due to the presence of an unconscious (repressed) old conflict which is activated by the stress produces the clinical picture of the crisis. The goal of this kind of treatment goes somewhat beyond the goals of recompensation treatment. In brief psychotherapy one attempts a limited restructuring of internal conflicts in order to prevent or mitigate the current clinical picture and subsequent decompensation. It is hoped that the result of the insight and working through in the limited sector will prevent similar stresses from producing another crisis. In this treatment model the specific stress which precipitated the present problem is not important in and of itself. It is important only because it activated an old conflict. The current social field (the family or other individuals in the interactional field) are not particularly important. The brief psychotherapy model is obviously oriented to the individual patient.

STRESS-ORIENTED MODEL

In the recompensation model and the brief psychotherapy model the focus of attention both theoretically and in terms of the treatment technics have been on the individual. The past decade or two have seen the development of an interest in the specific stress event (hazard). The word "crisis" has been associated with the contributions of Erich Lindemann and of Gerald Caplan.[25,8] These studies began with Lindemann's work with the victims of the Coconut Grove fire. He observed that the loss of a loved one is an event which in some precipitates a serious bereavement and psychopathologic reaction. Others react with the expectable amount of grief work and though it is a painful stress, master it and proceed without evidence of a psychiatric illness. From this and other work of his own, Gerald Caplan has evolved a view of crisis. The hazardous event poses a unique problem for the individual in crisis. It is not merely a generalized precipitant resulting in a decompensation or a symbol of repressed intrapsychic problems.

It presents a specific task to be mastered in adaptive fashion. If the approach is maladaptive, the crisis may result in regression and psychopathology which is an expression of the individual's past problems, as well as a result of the immediate crisis situation. The individual in crisis is viewed as being in a state of upset. The symptoms of crisis are evidences of tension, anxiety, hostility, or guilt. The individual may show confusion in his thinking and even in his perceptions if the crisis state is a severe one.

At this time of crisis the individual may work out a specific solution in a healthy direction, may develop new combinations of coping mechanisms or may learn new ego skills or roles. On the other hand, failure to master the crisis can only result in a reactivation of old problems and regressive behavior. The crisis is not an illness but may act as a precipitant of an illness.

The goal in crisis intervention is mastery through successful resolution of the specific tasks posed by the stress event. In addition, the crisis therapist wants to halt decompensation and restore the inoperative coping functions. Thus in the crisis of bereavement the critical task is "grief work." The grief work resolves the crisis in the direction of mastery of the loss without regression and symptoms of psychiatric illness. The therapist who accurately diagnoses the crisis will set his therapeutic efforts in the direction of helping the patient work through the grieving process. Thus the crisis intervention model goes beyond the individual and takes into account the stress event. The response to the precipitating event is seen as a current struggle for mastery in the direction of health rather than disease.

A SYSTEM-ORIENTED MODEL

The stress-oriented model has some advantage over the individual-oriented model in that it goes beyond the person himself to the occurrence of a specific event. However, both of these models ignore the fact that people live in a social situation. The social field in which the potential patient decompensates or reactivates an old conflict or has to deal with a new crisis has some effect on the outcome also. This social field may be a family or it may be a working group (an artificial family) or another subgroup within a community.[11,31] The social system itself may be in a state of equilibrium or it may be in a state of upset and disequilibrium. The field oriented model postulates that the outcome of a crisis may depend in part on the field (as well as on the individual, his past history and on the external stress). Indeed the very existence of a crisis may be induced by events in the social field.

In the Stanton and Schwartz study of a mental hospital, it was very clear that disequilibrium within the social system (the hospital staff) caused decompensation and disturbed behavior among individual psychiatric patients.[32] The symptoms of patients would disappear as soon as differences among staff members were ironed out.

Family-oriented crisis treatment is based on the same assumption. This assumption states that the illness and the symptoms of a family member are in part an expression of family conflicts. An individual in a state of crisis may be expressing an upset or disequilibrium within the family as a social unit.[1,2,3,6,7,19,24,29,34] An alternative view would be that the individual is being "scapegoated" and is expressing the upset of the entire family. A third point of view would be that the individual state of adaptation and equilibrium of any given family member depends upon reasonable stability within the family as a social unit. When the family is upset, this acts as a stress on all members of that group. Any member of the family who is especially susceptible to stress by virtue of previous conflicts, ego weakness and lack of ability to master stress may then decompensate. This concept maintains that there is a direct relationship between the individual state of mental health and the degree of conflict or equilibrium in the family. It can be applied broadly to include kinship networks, schools, industries and the entire communities as well as the nuclear family and the psychiatric hospital.[11,26,27,35]

Clinicians naturally emphasize the individual patient. The clinician is used to dealing with a single person who is experiencing distress—the identified patient. However, the social context in which all individuals function is frequently the source of the stress which precipitates the decompensation. Although the psychiatrist has often focused his major interest on the patient under stress, the fields of social science and social welfare have been concerned with the response to stress at the family level.[23] Both disciplines have been interested in the family's response to a variety of stresses including the effects of war on total populations, political persecutions, economic depressions and natural disasters. Other problems which have been studied from a family point of view are the problems of illegitimacy, suicide, alcoholism, and schizophrenia. A great deal of effort has come from the mental health professions and the findings of those who study families which include a schizophrenic patient have clearly shown that the identified patient is not the only sick person in the family. The family as a unit is disturbed and "abnormal." Individuals within the family other than the identified patient are also found to be sick people.

The family is not only the source of stress in many cases but has been a major resource in the resolution of stress. The family is the one social unit through which the troubles of all members usually filter. Each person brings home his problems, and he hopes for the understanding and support which will help him master life's struggles. The family is a potential source of strength for individuals who are bruised in the course of everyday living. When the family is functioning well as a stress mediating system, it is a source of enormous comfort and strength to its members. When the family fails in this function, it often adds to the burdens which individual members are already experiencing.

What happens to those families which fail to fulfill this stress mediating function for its members? They often add to the burden of the sick or troubled member by "scapegoating" or by extruding a sick member of the family in an attempt to maintain some sense of family integration. A member of a family who is labeled "mentally ill" is often such a scapegoat. As a result of his innate weaknesses, problems and deficiencies, as a result of external, internal and intrafamilial stresses, and as a result of the lack of help from the family, he may decompensate and become psychotic.

The Family Physician Treatment Model

Acute illnesses of which psychiatric emergencies are an example are a well-known phenomenon in medicine. It is not surprising therefore, to find a time-honored approach for dealing with such problems. Medical practice recognizes the social nature of these difficulties, particularly the critical involvement of the family. The

strategy for working with families in which a member is thought
to be in need of mental hospitalization was first derived from
general medical practice. The model has been one which we call
the "family practice" model.

Families represent the first line of care for a sick member. The
adults in the family make the first diagnosis of an illness. If the
problem is seen as a minor one, home care is immediately instituted. The family has competence to treat simple physical illness.
The home care consists largely of relieving the sick member temporarily of his normal responsibilities so that he can rest and use
simple remedies. When the patient fails to respond to rest and
aspirin, the problem is redefined as a "serious illness" and medical
attention is sought. At this point in the case of a physical illness,
the family level of tension usually rises out of concern for the
patient and because of their inability to manage the illness on
their own.

A generation ago the family doctor would have been called to
the home. Although "house calls" are less frequently used, the
present day action would be to have the family take the "patient"
to the doctor's office or the hospital emergency room. The wise
family physician approaches this situation by paying as much attention to the family as he does to the patient. His hope is to treat the
patient as an outpatient and avoid an unnecessary hospitalization.
With certain modifications, the family doctor's approach to physical
emergencies has been adapted to handle the family crisis of the
"mentally ill" member.

When a family decides that they have a "mentally ill" person in
the home, certain common assumptions are made. The label
signifies the existence of a mysterious, frightening, long-term disorder. The usual connotations are that the patient is no longer
responsible for his behavior or for carrying on normal responsibilities of living in a family. The mental illness label identifies the
sick member's behavior as irrational and unmanageable in the
family setting. Under these circumstances the family turns to a
psychiatrist (or is referred to a psychiatrist). The family expect
the psychiatrist to bring the patient back "to his senses" by treatment in a mental hospital. The job of the mental health professional who wants to convince the family that mental hospitalization

can be avoided is to show that these assumptions about the patient are not true. He needs to demonstrate to the family that the patient can be reasoned with and that sensible communication can take place. He needs to show that the patient is manageable in the family home. He accomplishes this task in two phases.

The first phase is the *examination*. The examination begins when the therapist takes control in a calm, reassuring manner. This attitude is in sharp contrast to the family's sense of worry and bewilderment. The therapist elicits information about the patient's problems from both the family and the patient in joint session. He explores and identifies recent stresses and the patient's experience, relating these problems to the current symptoms and behavior. This examination permits a catharsis of fears and frustration. It reduces tension in all members of the family. The patient is treated not as "mentally ill" but as a responsible, rational person, capable of communicating sensibly about his problems. The discussion of recent stresses invariably involves other family members. This permits the problems of the patient to be viewed as arising from current interpersonal relationships and not as a mysterious long-term illness which is purely within the patient. This approach makes it difficult to scapegoat the patient. It makes other members of the family responsible for their part in the current family problem and in the treatment of the social field as well as the patient.

The second phase of the process includes *diagnosis* and *prescription*. The patient's problem is defined as an acute disorder brought on by identifiable recent stress. The family and the patient are assured that the symptoms, the loss of functioning, and the patient's need for further family care are of a temporary nature. They are reassured that the patient, after brief treatment, will soon function at his previous level. The entire family is made responsible for completing certain tasks which are related to the present crisis. Drugs are prescribed to reduce anxiety, disabling symptoms, and to give the patient and other family members rest. The patient is told that he will soon be able to assume his usual responsibilities. The family is put into motion fulfilling assigned tasks. They are enjoined from those acts which will impede the patient's recovery. At times this means reducing pressure on the patient and at other times it means putting more pressure on the patient to function.

The family therapist (the doctor in the medical model) assures the family that he will be available until the patient is well on his way to recovery. Subsequent contacts are used to instruct the family and the patient in how to recognize signs of trouble at an earlier stage. The therapist anticipates that life will bring subsequent stress and hopes to teach the family how to deal with this expected stress more effectively. The availability of the family doctor for dealing with future problems is also made clear. This last step is an important assurance to the family. It represents an important component of emergency treatment which arose from the family doctor model of medical practice.

The family doctor's approach to medical emergencies offers a model which includes the concept of the family as the field in which crisis occurs and a concept of the family as a valuable ally in the resolution of crisis and decompensation. The family approach deals with the individual, with the crisis event itself, and with the social context in which crisis occurs. It offers a model of treatment which takes into account the individual, the specific stress and the social milieu. It includes the major contributions which have been derived from earlier stress treatment models.

Bibliography

1. Ackerman, Nathan W. *The Psychodynamics of Family Life: Diagnosis and Treatment of Family Relationships*. Basic Books, N. Y., 1958.

2. Bateson, G., Jackson, D. D., Haley, J. and Weakland, J. Toward a Theory of Schizophrenia. Behav. Sci. 1: 251-264, 1956.

3. Bell, J. E. Family Group Therapy. Pub. Hlth. Mon. No. 64. Dept. of Health Education and Welfare, Wash. D. C., 1961.

4. Bellak, Leopold and Small, Leonard. *Emergency Psychotherapy and Brief Psychotherapy*. New York: Grune & Stratton, 1965.

5. Bibring, E. Psychoanalysis and Dynamic Psychotherapies. J. Amer. Psychoanal. Ass. 11:745, 1954.

6. Boszormenyi-Nagy, I. The Concept of Schizophrenia from the Perspective of Family Treatment. Fam. Proc., 1, 103-113, 1962.

7. Bowen, M. A Family Concept of Schizophrenia. In: Jackson, D. D. (Ed): *The Etiology of Schizophrenia*. New York: Basic Books, 1960.

8. Caplan, Gerald. *Principles of Preventive Psychiatry*. New York: Basic Books, 1964.

9. Coleman, M. Donald. Emergency Psychotherapy. Progress in Psychotherapy, Vol. V: Reviews and Integrations, 1960.

10. Fenichel, Otto. *The Psychoanalytic Theory of Neurosis.* New York: W. W. Norton, 1945.

11 Flomenhaft, Kalman and Kaplan, David M. Clinical Significance of Current Kinship Relationships. Social Work 13:68–75, 1968.

12. Freud, S. Introduction to "Psychoanalysis of War Neuroses." London, 1921.

13. Freud, S. *The Problem of Anxiety.* New York: W. W. Norton, 1936.

14. Glass, Albert J. Psychiatry in the Korean Campaign: An Historical Review. U. S. Armed Forces Med. J. 4:1563-83, 1953.

15. Grinker, Roy R. and Spiegel, John. *Men Under Stress.* Philadelphia: Blakiston, 1945.

16. Hartmann, H. Technical Implications of Ego Psychology. Psychoanal. Quart. 20:31-43, 1951.

17. Hill, Rueben. *Families Under Stress.* New York: Harper & Bros., 1949.

18. Hill, Reuben. Social Stresses on the Family. Social Casework, Feb.-Mar., 1958.

19. Jackson, D. D. and Satir, V. A Review of Psychiatric Developments in Family Diagnosis and Therapy. In: Ackerman, N., Beatman, F. L., and Sherman, S. N. (Eds.): *Exploring the Base for Family Therapy.* New York: Family Service Association of America, 1961.

20. Kaplan, David M. A Concept of Acute Situational Disorders. Social Work, Vol. 7, No. 2, Apr. 1962.

21. Kaplan, David M. and Mason, Edward A. Maternal Reactions to Premature Birth Viewed as an Acute Emotional Disorder. Amer. J. Orthopsychiat., 30:539-47, 1960.

22. Koos, Earl L. *Families in Trouble.* New York: King's Crown Press, 1946.

23. Leichter, Hope J. and Mitchell, W. E. Kinship and Casework. New York: Russell Sage Fdn., 1967.

24. Lidz, T. and Fleck, S. Schizophrenia, Human Integration and Role of the Family. In: Jackson, D. D. (Ed.): *The Etiology of Schizophrenia.* New York: Basic Books, 1960.

25. Lindemann, Erich. Symptomatology and Management of Acute Grief. Amer. J. Psychiat. 101:141-48, 1944.

26. Meyer, Henry J., Jones, Wyatt and Borgatta, Edgar F. The Decision by Unmarried Mothers to Keep or Surrender Their Babies. Social Work, Vol. 1, No. 2 (1956), pp. 103-109.

27. N. Y. City Youth Board, Res. Dept. A Study of Some of the Characteristics of 150 Multiproblem Families. N. Y., 1957.

28. Querido, A. Early Diagnosis and Treatment Services. In: *Elements of a Community Mental Health Program.* New York: Millbank Mem. Fund, 1956, pp. 158-69.

29. Sampson, Harold, Towne, Robert D. and Messinger, Sheldon. *Schizophrenic Women.* New York: Atherton Press, 1964.

30. Semrad, Elvin V. and Zaslow, Stephen L. Assisting the Psychotic Patient to Recompensate. Ment. Hosp. 15:361-66, 1964.

31. Spiegel, John P. The Resolution of the Role Conflict Within the Family. Psychiatry. Vol. XX, No. 1 (1957), pp. 1–16.

32. Stanton, Alfred H. and Schwartz, Morris S. *The Mental Hospital.* New York: Basic Books, 1954.

33. Vincent, Clark E. Mental Health and the Family. J. of Marriage and the Family. 21:18-38, 1967.

34. Wynne, L. C. The Study of Intrafamilial Alignments and Splits in Exploratory Family Therapy. In: Ackerman, N. W., Beatman, F. L., and Sherman, S. N. (Eds.): *Exploring the Base for Family Therapy.* New York: Family Service Association of America, 1961.

35. Young, Leontine. *Out of Wedlock: A Study of the Problems of the Unmarried Mother and her Child.* New York: McGraw-Hill Book Co., 1954.

CHAPTER 2

The Technic of Family Crisis Therapy

The recent innovations and experiments in alternatives to hospitalization are predominantly secondary prevention measures which depend on principles of early case finding and brief treatment at times of crisis. The goals are to recompensate a patient who is acutely falling apart. These technics have been the subject of a number of recent contributions.[2,14,18,19,20] The treatment is known by a number of different names such as "brief psychotherapy," "crisis therapy," "emergency psychotherapy," "crisis intervention." It includes individual (one-to-one) psychotherapeutic technics, the use of psychoactive drugs, the utilization of social therapies, involvement with the family, and environmental manipulation. As an introduction to the process of family crisis therapy, the technical operations of individual crisis therapy will be reviewed.

Any form of psychotherapy depends upon a relationship between a patient in need of help and the helper. This is true for crisis therapy as well as long-term therapy.

In psychoanalysis the relationship is structured so as to promote regression and to permit the patient to experience the therapist unrealistically as each of the important people from his early life. Since the goals of depth treatment are alterations in personality structure by working out infantile conflicts which influence adult behavior, the analyst is relatively silent and makes himself anonymous and unseen, all for the purpose of permitting the development of a regressive transference neurosis. Only with the analysis and resolution of the transference neurosis in the terminal phase of treatment should he become a real person to the patient, i.e., the person that he really is. In contrast, the crisis therapist hopes to prevent rather than promote regression. His goals are rapid behavioral change and more adaptive solutions of acute problems. Regression is a process to be avoided. The posture he assumes in the relationship is one of presenting himself as skillful, helpful, and authoritative. He remains very much himself rather than an object from the past. Nonetheless, he cannot avoid being invested by the patient with the qualities which all of us attribute to a powerful helper.

GENERAL PRINCIPLES OF TREATING INDIVIDUALS IN CRISIS

As one reviews the recent literature on crisis intervention therapy or brief psychotherapy, eight principles and technics stand out as being commonly mentioned by all writers.

Use of the Patient's Expectations of Help from a Skilled Professional

In brief therapy the helper attempts to maintain a positive relationship, shows an empathic interest in the patient and emphasizes his availability. Although some call this maintaining a positive "transference," this is not really transference in the classic sense but rather the basic therapeutic alliance essential in all treatment relationships. In brief therapy the patient comes with expectations of help and relief from his pain and the treatment is more successfully conducted when the therapist keeps the work at this level. Most writers highlight the need for help to be easily available to those in crisis.[1]

Focus on Present Illness

The therapist emphasizes the present symptoms, the precipitating event which sets off the current crisis. The work is at the surface or conscious level of mental functioning. The goals must be realistic, i.e., the achievement of a recompensation in an acutely decompensating patient. It would be inappropriate to deal with problems from the past or with long-term patterns of chronically disturbed behavior. The past is explored to elucidate its influence on the present and to discover previous similar crises.

Active Role

The therapist is active rather than passive. The passivity of the psychoanalyst is necessary and useful to achieve the goal of a regressive transference neurosis, but it is not the goal of crisis treatment to achieve such regression. The therapist doing brief treatment actively reassures and structures the content to the present problem, as well as interprets nonverbal clues offered by the patient. Semrad stresses the importance of the therapist as a representative of reality and points out the usefulness of discouraging the patient's self-destructive patterns or regressive behavior.[19] The brief therapist takes an authoritarian and directive role in opposition to regression and self destructiveness.

Eclecticism and Pragmatism

One approach that will *not* work in brief therapy is rigid adherence to a preconceived method of treatment. The brief therapist must be willing to use a variety of technics and adopt a pragmatic approach which might well be characterized as "whatever works is useful." Reassurance is cited by all writers as an important technic. Others highlight the importance of suggestion.[3] Most emphasize the utilization of emotional catharsis in conjunction with taking a history of the recent precipitating factors. Others speak of the necessity for the brief therapist to be a counsellor, to offer guidance, advice, and education. The brief therapist is encouraged to let the patient identify with him as one of the technics for increasing mastery over the current crisis and developing new coping skills.

Enhancing Self-Esteem

The individual patient in crisis is subject to considerable diminution of self-esteem. He often shows the frank symptoms of depression. If not clinically depressed, he frequently feels bad or inadequate about himself because he does not seem to be able to solve his problems alone. The very act of going to a professional for help produces a diminution of self-esteem. It is therefore part of the work of brief therapy to help patients feel better about themselves by positive reinforcement and praise for successful accomplishment and healthy coping behavior.

Social and Environmental Manipulation

Another element of brief therapy is active manipulation of the environment. Many authors suggest that it is advisable for a social worker to see the family for this purpose.[11] Historically the word "manipulation" has had a bad connotation. It is considered out of place in intensive individual psychotherapy aimed towards insight and the resolution of intrapsychic conflict. In brief therapy aimed towards solving an immediate problem and rapid behavioral change, manipulation is a respectable and effective technic. In marital crisis it may be effective for the spouse who is not labeled "patient" to ventilate and express the other side of the story and then for the therapist to suggest technics which will reduce the pressure on the patient.

Utilization of Drugs

Many who write about brief therapy encourage the use of psychoactive drugs. Although we do not know the specific ana-tomical sites nor the metabolic pathways by which these drugs alleviate symptoms, empirically they are extremely useful. The reduction of tension and the consequent availability of problem-solving capacities make the drugs a useful adjunct to brief therapy.

Termination with Open Door

The termination in brief therapy is one which should be planned from the very beginning. The initial arrangement for treatment should include a reasonably specific arrangement about the length of treatment and termination. The avoidance of regressive trans-ference and the attempt to keep the therapist a real object permits relatively rapid termination. The termination should end on a positive note with praise for the accomplishments and reinforce-ment of more adaptive behavior. It should also be accomplished without putting the stamp of finality on the relationship. Brief therapists encourage an open door type of termination with the patient realizing that he can return for help with future crisis.

It can be seen that the technics of individually oriented crisis therapy depend upon a patient with a recent crisis (rather than long-term problems), his faith in a professional therapist, and the utilization of a directive and active technic by the therapist in-cluding a detailed history of the recent problem, an emotional catharsis, support and suggestion or manipulation. These technics seem effective. While there are very few studies reported where systematic follow-up and evaluation of crisis therapy has been done, the clinical impressions of those who report such approaches to treatment are that it is effective. Among those who use crisis therapy to avoid hospitalization (see Chapter 1), there is uniform reporting of avoidance of hospitalization in from 50 to 75 per cent of cases seen. Levy in his report of crisis therapy hospitalizes an exceedingly small number of those seen.[11] The experience of the Colorado Psychiatric Hospital Emergency Psychiatric Service is that the percentage of patients hospitalized when crisis therapy is available drops from 52 per cent to 26 per cent.[9] It is hoped that the systematic evaluation and follow-up of patients treated by family crisis therapy as compared with those treated by hospitalization will give us reasonably systematic and replicable as well as generalizable data from which to defend or reject the further utilization of crisis therapy.

Jerome Frank has systematically studied the process and effects of outpatient psychotherapy using a variety of models of treatment.[6] He emphasizes the nonspecific factors which are effective in changing behavior, reducing symptoms and in improving disease. These nonspecific factors are found in all kinds of formal and informal psychotherapies, among primitive healers as well as the sophisticated professionals. These nonspecific factors might be listed as follows:

(1) The healer is a socially sanctioned expert.
(2) There is a giving of hope and an expectation of help.
(3) Ritual is a part of the healing.
(4) There is a review of the past. History taking is part of the ritual.
(5) There is an emotional catharsis which is important in producing attitudinal or behavioral change.
(6) The sufferer is susceptible to influence by the healer because he is in pain.

It will immediately be apparent that these nonspecific factors are important to the model of brief therapy. Although the crisis therapist may deal with specific problems utilizing his professional knowledge of individual human behavior and conflict, the nonspecific factors are invariably present. One might even be tempted to deemphasize the content of the particular crisis and say that almost any crisis would be subject to improvement under the conditions of the nonspecific factors.

The crisis therapy technics reviewed to this point have been focused on individual patients. If family members are seen, it is for

collaborative work, to obtain additional history, or to alter the
environment in which the patient lives. The assumption is that it is
the patient who is sick. However, decompensation does not arise
or continue in an interactional vacuum. Over the past decade social
psychiatrists and psychologists have become increasingly aware of
the family's part in precipitating, maintaining or reversing emotional illness. Querido suggests, "any removal of a mentally disturbed patient from his social background implies the sidestepping
of the nucleus of the problem."[17] Though we are aware of the
importance of the individual's past history in rendering him susceptible to regression and decompensation, it is the family setting in
which most crises evolve.[4]

For this reason our interest has shifted from individual crisis
treatment to family crisis treatment. Although other clinicians
have intermittently seen whole families at times of crisis, we are not
aware of any systematic attempt to test the value of treating whole
families (rather than individuals). This has been the goal of the
Family Treatment Unit. Before describing the technics for treating
families in crisis, we should define the population. The population
from which a random sample is drawn for family crisis treatment
consists of all those deemed in immediate need of admission to
Colorado Psychiatric Hospital who live in a family and who live in
the Denver Metropolitan area.

In addition, they must enter voluntarily. We define living in a
family as living with one other person between the ages of 16 to
60 to whom the patient is related by blood or marriage. The
Denver metropolitan area includes the four counties covering a
travel radius of one hour from the hospital. Of the 1,000 admissions
each year to CPH (a short-stay hospital with an average length
of hospitalization of twenty-four days), approximately 50 per cent
meet the above criteria. On all such admissions the resident psychiatrist, who does the evaluation for admission in the emergency
room, telephones the Family Treatment Unit after he has decided
that the patient needs to be hospitalized but before he tells the
family of his decision. With his telephone call, an envelope is
opened which says "yes" or "no". If the envelope says "no", the
patient is immediately admitted to CPH. If the reply is affirmative,
the Family Treatment Unit immediately takes responsibility for the
patient. Family crisis treatment rather than hospitalization is un-

dertaken. Those hospitalized constitute a pool of potential controls from which a sample is drawn equal in size and matched by group to the group of patients treated by family crisis therapy.

FAMILY CRISIS TREATMENT

The technic for family crisis treatment may be outlined under seven headings.[15]

Immediate Aid

As soon as a family is accepted by the random selection process, the members are seen *at once* by the Family Treatment Unit team. One of the Family Treatment Unit team members is always on call and is available around the clock seven days a week. New cases may be taken either during regular working hours or at night or on the weekend. The patient who is in the emergency room is seen within a few minutes and is told that help will be available immediately and around the clock so long as it is needed. The mere promise of help gives the patient and whatever family members are present the conviction that there will be some relief from the tension which has been so troublesome in the immediate past.

Defining the Crisis as a Family Problem

From the time that the Family Treatment Unit has its first contact with the patient, the idea is conveyed that the problem involves all the family members. The family therapist reinforces this definition by immediately calling together all available household members for the first meeting. The family is told that they will be seen as a group. When other caretakers have been involved with the family (e.g. ministers, physicians, social workers, probation officers, etc.), they are immediately contacted and invited to work with the Family Treatment Unit in the treatment of the family as well as to continue their relationship with the family after crisis therapy. The first meeting occurs with the family. This sets the stage for an approach involving the family.

Focus on the Current Crisis

The therapist who has gathered the family together asks initially for a statement of the present problem. Although this may be presented from different points of view and consequently differing

stories may emerge, a clearer picture of the immediate situation is
gained from seeing the whole family. Missing details or distortions
in the story offered by the identified patient are corrected by other
family members present. That which is kept secret by parents is
often revealed by children.[1] Children are invariably brought in to
at least the first or second family session. Those below age ten
may not continue in the family crisis therapy, depending upon the
type of problem. However, it has been our experience that it is
valuable to see the entire family together as early as possible and
that young children offer information about the family problems
not always available from the adults.

This elucidation of the present crisis also offers opportunity for
consensual validation or for highlighting areas of distortion and
disagreement. The first session if conducted late at night, does not
have to be prolonged. Here the nonspecific factors begin to show
their effect—the promise of help from a socially sanctioned expert
and the opportunity for explaining the crisis. A half hour more or
less in the middle of the night with a return interview scheduled
the following morning will often keep the family intact and the
patient out of the hospital. Recently we saw a sixteen year old girl
together with her mother, stepfather and a family friend at 2:00
A.M. The girl was brought to the emergency room ostensibly for
rebelliousness and a suicide attempt. The mother had been called
home from work late in the afternoon by an aunt to whom the
teenage daughter had telephoned a suicide threat. The mother
found the house locked and the daughter inside, called her husband
home from work, broke into the house and with the help of a
family friend, brought the girl to the emergency room. The first
activity in the emergency room was gastric lavage to remove the
remains of 50 aspirin. This was followed by a period of medical
observation and supportive care. When it was determined that the
girl had not suffered serious poisoning, she was referred to the
psychiatric resident who felt that she needed immediate admission
to CPH. She fell into the FTU sample and was seen within a few
minutes of the call to the FTU. In the initial session with the girl,
mother, stepfather and family friend, the young lady verbalized
her complaints against her mother's excessive nagging control of
her dating behavior. The mother presented the story that the girl
had been sexually promiscuous for many months and was now

dating an ex-convict. Mother was convinced that the girl would soon be pregnant. The daughter wanted to drop out of school and live with her young man with or without the benefit of marriage. The father sat passively expressing nonverbally the role he had been taking for several years in this conflict between mother and daughter. The family friend (an older woman) affirmed the mother's complaints. The daughter then described how mother knew of her promiscuity and had in fact, subtly encouraged it. The mother then told the story of her own adolescence, the unsatisfactory home situation, the promiscuity, a premarital pregnancy and her escape from home through an early marriage. The family had been involved in this crisis for seven hours. After the elucidation of the current situation, the family therapist suggested that it was late and everyone was tired and needed sleep and offered another interview early the next morning. Once the problem was placed in perspective, it no longer seemed insurmountable. The family agreed that they could manage the situation better with a little rest. They staggered home and appeared at the appointed time next morning, fresher, more comfortable and obviously more capable of working on the family problem.

Within the first twenty-four to thirty-six hours the Family Treatment Unit schedules a home visit in the family home. This has a variety of advantages. First of all the team sees family interaction in vivo. This is especially valuable in observing parent-child interaction. Information about the family composition and family functioning is obtained in the home which may be overlooked or unavailable at a family group session in our own offices. Equally important is the effect on the therapeutic alliance. The home visit convinces the family that the FTU really is interested, really does mean to offer help above and beyond scheduled appointments in our own offices. Furthermore, families display their strengths as well as their weaknesses in the home setting. The relationship is thus based on all aspects of family functioning, not just the decompensation associated with a crisis.

The goal is to gain entrance into the family within the first twenty-four hours, to place responsibility for the patient's symptoms on the family and to relieve the immediate tension sufficiently to proceed with work on the family crisis.

General Prescription

The immediate activity in family crisis therapy is to reduce the level of tension and upset which invariably accompanies any effort on the part of the family to bring one of its members to a mental hospital. There is value in using the model of the family physician in this type of treatment. Although specific indicators of a crisis and steps in resolving the crisis have been offered by a few investigators (for example, the crisis of bereavement[12] and the crisis of the birth of a premature child,[18]) for the most part the treatment of crisis is nonspecific and directed towards symptoms rather than etiology. The general activity is directed towards interference with regression. In the first session and in a subsequent meeting or two, psychotic symptoms on the part of the patient are defined as the identified patient's attempts to communicate. The family crisis therapist will call on his clinical experience to interpret these communications to the family. In addition, he will encourage more adaptive behavior and more adaptive styles of communication.

The psychoactive drugs can also reduce the tension of patients and family members. Tranquilizers or energizers may be given to diminish excessive anxiety or to treat a disturbance in mood. They are prescribed for any family member who needs them—often not the identified patient. If it is necessary to maintain adequate supervision or control of a patient whose behavior is out of control—an acute schizophrenic or an acutely delirious patient, we may keep the patient in a "holding bed" in the General Hospital Emergency Room for a few hours.[10] This has been a resource which has been used less than ten times among our group of 150 patients. It often avoids an unnecessary psychiatric hospitalization. It is far easier to discharge a patient from a short-stay emergency room bed than from a mental hospital. Once admitted to the hospital, a system of routines takes over and the patient has to have a comprehensive work-up. The tension reduction and adequate sleep effected by drugs and rest, either in the family home or the emergency room, interferes with pathologic regression and permits previously unavailable problem-solving ego capacities to be used.

Specific Prescription

The specific prescription for the crisis in question depends on the acute situation. We assume that a series of events within the family have led to the decompensation of a susceptible family member. These events begin with a change in family equilibrium. Jackson has postulated a theory of family homeostasis which defines a family crisis as the result of an upset in the normal level of balance within the family.[7] This change of equilibrium may be due to a change in family composition (e.g., birth of a child, visit of an in-law), a change in role performance of some member, or a change in circumstances requiring a new role (e.g., a developmental crisis or a physical illness on the part of one family member). Such changes require a reshuffling of role assignments within the family. A family crisis may occur when an important role is not being filled or when the family member assigned to the role cannot or will not do what the family demands.

Family tasks are proposed as a step toward the resolution of the specific crisis. The family is given as an initial task the working out as a group of some activity related to the current crisis. In the family crisis which often occurs around adolescents moving toward adult independence or adult sexual behavior, the family may be given the task of working out in a conference, rules for dating or privileges which are age appropriate and consistent with the privileges afforded peers. If the crisis has to do with the performance of household tasks, a mother may be given the task of cleaning her kitchen. In the case of a work or school phobia, the task of the family is to get the identified patient to face the phobic situation.[16] When feasible, the chosen task is an activity in which the whole family can participate. Then, the family is expected to focus on the task rather than on the symptoms and the conflicts.

Identification of Role Conflicts and Renegotiation

By this stage of therapy the family has usually been seen for an office visit or two plus the home visit. For the most part, there has been a radical change in the clinical picture of the identified patient and of other family members. The calming effects of reassurance, support, catharsis, and drugs have taken hold.

The family crisis therapy which has been carried on by the Family Treatment Unit has utilized an average of five office visits, a home visit, two or three phone calls and, if applicable, a collateral contact or two with the referring agencies or with other social agencies which have been involved with the family prior to the crisis. For the first two or three days, contact is maintained daily but after things have settled down it is possible to begin tapering off the frequency of contacts. This takes an average of two and a half weeks. There is a range of course, some cases being settled and ready for termination within a week, others go on a month or more. It should also be mentioned that in many cases it becomes apparent that a member of the extended family is very much involved in the current crisis.[5] Where this is found to be the case, the extended family member is included in the treatment. This may be a grandmother living close to the family or may be a parent living several hundred miles away. In one case the family crisis had to do with a married man's father living three hundred miles away who persisted in infantilizing his son by discouraging his efforts to be financially independent and repetitively offering to pay the bills and provide money. The contacts with his father were by telephone, although at one point he made a trip to Denver and was interviewed in person.

By this point the family orientation has made each member aware of his responsibility to the family as a unit. Each member sees that his actions have significant effect upon others in the family. By some exploration of the events leading up to the crisis, the team discovers some of the ways in which the family met each member's needs more successfully before the crisis. The focus at this point may shift from the symptomatic member of the family (the identified patient) to a family member who is able and willing to make compromises. The family is confronted as a group with their responsibility for compromise and change to meet and cope with whatever the new problem may be. Often there is a backlog of anger over chronic conflicts and past failures. During the crisis no one may want to compromise and retaliation may seem more important than improvement.

In other cases (see the chapter on marital crisis) the couple may wish to continue a relationship which others would call pathologic but which has lasted for years. In such cases, crisis therapy means nothing more than getting the couple back to the previous level of adjustment.

Management of Future Crises

By the end of the crisis treatment, the family is generally ready for discharge from active treatment. The goals of resolution of the crisis and return of the family to the precrisis level of functioning can be achieved in this length of time. Long-term problems are not expected to be resolved. This family approach may teach a family that there are ways of solving a problem other than putting one member of the family in the hospital. It may set the family on the road towards more adaptive management of crises. However, the termination should take into account two factors. One of these is that the crisis treatment may have brought into prominence individual or interactional problems for which a patient or a portion of the family may have become motivated for help. This necessitates referral for such problems. For example, a marital crisis may be dealt with in this kind of treatment but the resolution of long-term difficulties between a husband and wife which is sought by both, may be handled by referral to a marriage counsellor or an appropriate social agency. The treatment of a family in which the identified patient was the mother of two adolescent sons dealt with the immediate crisis of the mother's wish to get a divorce. During the course of treatment the seventeen year old boy indicated that he had been having a great deal of trouble in school and in relationships with his girl friend. He was referred for individual therapy of his sexual anxieties. These referrals, when they occur, take place at the end of crisis treatment. Several steps make referrals more effective. They include: (1) contact of the agency to whom a referral is being made by a member of the treatment team to appraise them of the referral and to offer information; (2) giving the family or individual, specific information and telephone numbers for making the contact (but not making the contact for them); (3) sending a written report of our contacts and information to the agency to which the referral is being made; (4) a follow-up contact with the family or family member to see that contact has been made; (5) continued availability to the agency to which referral is being made for consultation about the family. When a referral includes these steps, it generally "takes." When some or all are missing and the patient is merely handed a telephone number, we have had only a forty per cent success rate in the referral process.

The other aspect of termination involves an open door. The family is invited to contact the Family Treatment Unit again in the future should crises arise. As part of our research and evaluation we also explain to the family that we will be contacting them at three months, six months, eighteen months, and yearly thereafter. Not all clinical units doing family crisis therapy will be involved in such an evaluation process. However, we have been impressed with the importance of terminating on the note of our availability for future crises.

In this description of the technic of family crisis therapy, one is impressed with its similarity to the posture and attitude of the general practitioner or family physician. The general practitioner's first activity is his examination of the patient. He calmly takes control. His manner expresses his competence and confidence in contrast to the family's sense of helplessness and bewilderment. Likewise, the therapist reviews the symptoms of the patient jointly with the family members and the patient. He reviews current family problems and includes the patient as one of the informants in this situation. This process permits an important cathartic release on the part of all members, an expression of the feelings of anxiety, anger and frustration. By including the patient, the examiner demonstrates that he considers him to be both rational and controllable despite his "sick" label. The review of current family problems and stresses helps to make the symptoms and behavior of the patient understandable as a reaction to these stresses and not the result of a mysterious and frightening mental illness. Through the process the therapist helps the patient to be taken off the hook as the scapegoat and to make his problems understandable as a family problem in which most members play a part and have responsibility.

As the symptoms become understandable in the context of current stresses, the prescription phase begins. The therapist begins his prescription by indicating that hospitalization is not required and emphasizes the importance to the family and the patient of all members continuing to function responsibly. This is taken as proof of continued family membership on the part of the patient and as evidence that the identified patient will not continue to be an unreasonable caretaking responsibility for other members of the family. Another aspect of the prescription may be the assignment of drugs to any family member who requires them to control symptoms and to encourage functioning. The family is involved in obtaining the drugs and in seeing to it that the "patient" takes the medication as prescribed. The family is encouraged to treat the identified patient not as crazy or irrational but as a responsible individual who will soon be restored to functioning. The family is specifically enjoined from those actions that contribute to conflict and symptoms either in the form of unrealistic demands or in the form of offering the identified patient too much protection which encourages regression.

Typically the family responds quickly to this process of treatment accepting the therapist's definition of the "patient" as a temporarily disturbed but not crazy member who is amenable to outpatient and home care. A home visit which clarifies the current situation, encourages all members to function and confirms the therapist's availability and interest. As the family regains confidence in their ability to control the situation, they can resume responsibility for the care of the temporarily upset member. The patient can be discharged from treatment once he has established that he is on the way to resuming his pre-crisis level of functioning. At that point the therapist makes clear his ready availability for future crises and avoids the traditional psychiatric termination of treatment so characteristic of long-term psychotherapy. Once the recompensation has begun, contacts with the patient and family are used to teach them how to recognize the early signs of trouble which future stress situations are likely to arouse, and to impress on them the importance of seeking help before things get out of hand again. Subsequent crises are often handled successfully over the telephone or in one or two interviews. Caretaker consultation is offered to those who have contact with the patient and family in order to deal with the caretaker's anxiety which might lead him to regard the mental hospital as a solution to problems.

The point that should be stressed about crisis therapy individual or family in its orientation, is that it must be available when another crisis occurs. In crisis treatment we do not delude ourselves that brief treatment produces personality pattern changes in the patient or permanent changes in the family. The goals are those of avoiding hospitalization with its tendency to promote regression and chronicity, to blunt some of the weapon value of symptoms and to demonstrate to families that they can resolve crises more economically and function more efficiently. But life itself produces crises. There is no treatment which will avoid or eliminate the distress of the usual problems of living. Crisis treatment is efficient and effective in resolving an acute situation. Furthermore, it teaches those to whom it is administered that relatively brief help with future crises can avoid serious consequences. Hospitals have found that brief treatment can get the acutely ill out of the hospital rapidly but that they must be prepared for readmissions which will be equally brief.[19] The revolving door policy of the hospital has resulted in a series of brief hospitalizations for many patients. However, the total time spent in the hospital is far less than under the old state mental hospital custody orientation. Likewise, the crisis clinic must be prepared to admit former patients rapidly when new crises arise.

Bibliography

1. Ackermann, Nathan W. *Treating the Troubled Family.* New York: Basic Books, 1966.
2. Bellak, Leopold and Small, Leonard. *Emergency Psychotherapy and Brief Psychotherapy.* New York: Grune & Stratton, 1965.
3. Coleman, M. Donald and Zwerling, Israel. The emergency psychiatric clinic: a flexible way of meeting community mental health needs. Amer. J. Psychiat. 115:980, 1959.
4. Ferber, Andrew et al. Current family structure: psychiatric emergencies and patient fate. Arch. Gen. Psychiat. 16:659-67, 1967.
5. Flomenhaft, Kalman and Kaplan, David M. Clinical significance of current kinship relationships. Social Work. 13:68-75, 1968.
6. Frank, Jerome. *Persuasion and Healing.* Baltimore: Johns Hopkins Press, 1961.
7. Jackson, Don D. Family rules: marital quid pro quo. Arch. Gen. Psychiat 12:589-94, 1965.
8. Kaplan, David M. and Mason, Edward A. Maternal reactions to premature birth viewed as an acute emotional disorder. Amer. J. Orthopsychiat. 30:539-47, 1960.
9. Kritzer, Herbert and Langsley, Donald G. Training for emergency psychiatric services. J. Med. Educ. 42:1111-15, 1967.
10. Kritzer, Herbert and Pittman, Frank S. Twenty-four hour hospitalization in a general emergency room setting. Read at Amer. Psychiat. Assn. Annual Meeting, Detroit, May 11, 1967.
11. Levy, Richard A. Six-Session outpatient therapy. Hosp. Community Psychiat. 17:340-43, 1966.
12. Lindemann, Erich. Symptomatology and management of acute grief. Amer. J. Psychiat. 101:141-48, 1944.
13. Mendel, Werner M. Effect of length of hospitalization on rate and quality of remission from acute psychotic episodes. J. Nerv. Ment. Dis. 143:226-233, 1966.

14. Parad, Howard J. *Crisis Intervention: Selected Readings.* New York: Family Service Association of America, 1965.

15. Pittman, Frank S., Flomenhaft, Kalman, DeYoung, Carol, Kaplan, David and Langsley, Donald G. Techniques of family crisis therapy. In: Masserman, Jules (Ed.): *Current Psychiatric Therapies.* New York: Grune & Stratton, 1966. pp. 187-196.

16. Pittman, Frank S. III, Langsley, Donald G. and DeYoung, Carol D. Work and school phobias: a family approach. Amer. J. Psychiat. 124–1535–41, 1968.

17. Querido, A. Early diagnosis and treatment services. In: *Elements of a Community Mental Health Program.* New York: Millbank Memorial Fund, 1956. pp. 158-69.

18. Rapaport, Lydia. Crisis-Oriented short term casework. Social Service Review. 41:31-43, 1967.

19. Semrad, Elvin V., Binstock, William A. and White, Burton. Brief psychotherapy. Amer. J. Psychother. 20:576-599, 1966.

20. Wolberg, Lewis R. *Short Term Psychotherapy.* New York: Grune & Stratton, 1965.

CHAPTER 3

Selected Topics in Family Crisis Therapy

TEAM OPERATIONS IN FAMILY CRISIS THERAPY

Although family crisis therapy could be carried on by a single therapist, we have found it wiser to use a treatment team. The intensity of this type of work, the demands of 24 hour availability and the varied skills required to deal with families in crisis have all entered into this decision.

There was a time when team operation meant clear differences in the function of each member. In the child guidance movement as well as the mental hospital, the psychiatrist conducted the examination and treatment of the identified patient. The social worker would see the family for anamnesis and/or collaborative therapy designed to manipulate the environment. The psychologist would do testing of the identified patient, occasionally would do collaborative psychotherapy. Nurses worked only on inpatient units where they gave medication, custodial care and kept records of the patient's daily behavior.

Today's mental health professionals all get better training than they received a few decades ago. Psychiatrists, psychologists, social workers, and nurses all receive good grounding in the psychodynamics of individual behavior, psychopathology, and the effects of interaction in social systems. Although each discipline offers different skills and emphases as well as proficiency and experience, these four professions have far more in common than the differences among them. In working with individuals or groups, the psychiatrist finishes his training with more years of clinical experience, but the other three groups are including clinical skills in individual and group therapy to an ever-increasing extent. Clinical psychology is moving towards post-doctoral training for clinicians who wish to treat patients more or less independently. Psychiatric social workers now require at least Master's degree training and many doctoral programs are being established. This profession has always emphasized supervised clinical experience in casework with individuals and groups. Psychiatric nursing is also moving towards master's level training for the clinical specialist and a few doctoral programs are in existence.

The composition of the clinical team of the Family Treatment Unit may not be the same as groups working in other mental health centers. We have said nothing about activity therapists, non-psychiatric physicians, pastoral counsellors, indigenous nonprofessionals and other groups involved in mental health treatment programs. We feel that any comments about the functions of these other groups would be pure speculation since we have had no experience with other than the four basic groups whose functions will be dealt with in this chapter. In fact, our treatment of the role of the psychologist may well be inadequate since our psychologist has been a social rather than clinical psychologist. His functions have been more concerned with evaluation and research than clinical work. However the section on the role of the psychologist will attempt to deal with the function of clinical as well as social psychologists since most of us have worked with clinical psychologists in other settings.

Much has been written about the advantage of conjoint family therapy conducted by two or more therapists, but this is even more true for family crisis therapy.[1,3,6,7] The demands of emergency treatment are great when one considers the highly disturbed behavior of patients felt to be in need of immediate hospitalization and the distress of their families. It is necessary to intervene rapidly and skillfully. Such patients and their families present themselves with a seething cauldron of interpersonal conflicts, disturbed behavior and conflicting information. The family's feelings and attitudes are demonstrated at a very fast clip and the more rapidly the therapist can comprehend their significance, the more effective the treatment. The demands on the professional are to digest and integrate a great deal of individual and interactional data within a short time. This is facilitated by the use of two therapists. While one team member reads a lengthy chart of past contacts with the hospital, the other may be telephoning a community agency for current information on the patient and family. Two therapists can protect each other from focusing only on the patient while important attitudes and feelings of other family members are overlooked. The observation of Wynne is applicable: "In families with many members, and in families which are especially fragmented and disorganized, the use of co-therapists does help the therapist to survive. He can be freer in his reflective capacities, not have to be defensively managerial, and can call upon the resources of the additional pair of eyes and ears in keeping up with the events of the therapy."[8]

The team has occasionally found it helpful to interview several family members separately, a function more easily accomplished with co-therapists provided there is a conference of the therapists before proceeding. In Multiple Impact Therapy, MacGregor regards the entire family unit as the patient, but "each member also needs to be regarded as an individual with problems and abilities that are relatively independent of the family—a need difficult to fulfill adequately in group sessions with all the other family members present."[5] How much is revealed in both individual and family sessions must be tempered as the family members may take the conjoint session as license to reveal all family secrets. This may be troublesome in crisis treatment where goals are limited and some family matters are best kept under wraps.

With acutely disturbed families "the reassuring presence of two workers may serve to diminish fears of chaotic family dissolution."[1] Working in pairs also allows more leeway in the manner each therapist uses to relate to the family. While one team member assumes an authoritarian and confronting position, the other therapists can take on a supportive role. During the interview the therapist can correct each other on the spot. Free discussion between the therapists of their differences can be an eye-opener and a model for families who are frightened of airing their differences.

In short-term therapy with families we have not seen some of the intrateam conflict seen in long-term therapy. In contrast, "where family treatment goes on for a long time and where deep exploration and meaningful changes in the family process are our goals, the team process becomes a critical ingredient in the entire therapy process."[6]

A third member of the clinical team often views the family from behind a one-way mirror, serving in a quarterback role to evaluate the process in the family interview. Being out of the room provides the viewer-consultant with greater objectivity in examining the process. Treatment stalemates in which the therapists keep repeating a particular tack with no response from the family can be quickly spotted this way. In the throes of the interview situation, the therapists are sometimes unable to detect and resolve these stalemates. On the rare occasion when the therapists are not fully appreciating the depth of a depression or suicidal intent, the third person's observations or comments cannot wait till the end of the interview and an interruption for a team conference may be in order. This is more relevant for crisis treatment with its rapid tempo than long-term family treatment where stalemates and resistances are more easily tolerated.

Knowledge of all active cases is necessary because of the 24 hour availability and the rotation of night and weekend call for all team members. For this rotation the Family Treatment Unit has utilized all team members. Medical coverage must also be available for medication and physical illness. The two physicians of this project, the Director and full-time psychiatrist have either been available themselves, or have arranged for medical back-up.

In actual practice any of the three members of the clinical team may have made the initial contact. If the first call is at night or on a weekend when only one team member is available, that person will make the first contact with the family and proceed in the usual approach to family crisis treatment. Where a medical opinion is needed, one of the two physicians is called if the team member doing the first contact is not an M.D. By the second contact, other team members have been brought into the treatment for subsequent contacts, including the home visit. The clinical skills of the psychiatric social worker or the nurse have permitted them to take a high degree of responsibility for independent work with adequate back-up, supervision and consultation.[2]

ROLE SPECIALIZATION IN THE TREATMENT TEAM

Although the technics of family crisis therapy have been carried on by professionals from different disciplines (social work, nursing, psychology, and medicine) in a generalist tradition, there are certain functions which might be called "specialized." We have focused on the technics which might be used by any mental health professional because better training has expanded (some have termed it "blurred") roles. The psychologic therapies—individual and group—have been increasingly utilized by professions other than medicine but certain functions such as the treatment of organic disease and prescribing of medication have remained the function of the physician. The laws relating to medical practice have required that a licensed physician be the only person permitted to prescribe or to carry on certain physical treatments.

Law alone has not been the sole arbiter of practice. In the field of psychologic testing, the clinical psychologist has generally been the only team member with training and experience in the administration and interpretation of tests. The nurse has almost always been a woman and often the only female member of the treatment team. Therefore to pretend that each member of the treatment team functions exactly and invariably as does each other member is a fiction.

The *psychiatrist* in his training encounters two divergent, even opposing traditions. He is trained first in the medical tradition that it is his responsibility to actively "cure" the patient or alleviate his symptoms. As a medical doctor, he suggests, directs, advises, operates, manipulates, and prescribes. The psychiatric resident in his training as a psychotherapist must curb his impulses to act and learn to be a passive listener whose goals are acceptance and understanding. Out of the insight-oriented psychotherapy may come knowledge which the patient may use to alter his behavior himself. The physician as a crisis therapist must combine both skills. He must be able to listen, accept and understand, but he must do it quickly since crisis therapy is by definition, brief therapy. He should have enough skill as a psychotherapist to quickly diagnose the psychodynamic conflicts which the patient and family do not understand. Frequently these conflicts are not "interpreted" or made conscious—the inactive listener must understand, but he may keep his understanding to himself. To interpret deep conflicts or to encourage regressive transference experiences is *not* the goal of the crisis therapist. Instead his activity resembles that of other physicians. He suggests, directs, advises, manipulates the environment and prescribes medication. Thus, threading his way between the model of the active general physician and the inactive psychotherapist is the first special problem of the psychiatrist. This too is not confined to the psychiatrist, since the psychologist, social worker and nurse are often taught the passive role of psychotherapist.

The specific activity which the physician-psychiatrist will have to carry on is the prescribing of drugs and the administration of physical treatment such as electroshock therapy. The law requires that only a physician prescribe or administer medical treatment. The laws establishing certain mental health centers also may require that a physician take responsibility for the treatment programs (though not necessarily the administration of the center). Thus the physician cannot avoid the medical-legal responsibility specific to his role. It would be fiction, however, to pretend that other team members have nothing to say about medication or other physical treatment. They will acquire knowledge about drugs, about side-effects as well as appropriate dose levels and will often have suggestions for the physician about pharmacotherapy.

The psychiatrist will find that other tasks are specific to his role. It is always helpful for the family in crisis to realize that a physician is involved with the team, since they know from past experience what "doctors" represent. The family may only need to meet the M.D. briefly to realize that he is involved in the team treatment and available when needed. In addition, contact with other M.D.'s is usually made by the psychiatrist member of the team. Physicians are more likely to share information with other physicians. Additionally if the "patient" was referred by a physician for hospitalization, the decision to not hospitalize will be more readily accepted from another physician. Medical men are not yet accustomed to the operation of the mental health team, and all team members will find that there is value in physicians dealing with physicians, social workers with social workers, etc.

Just as the physician brings the tradition of prescribing drugs to his work on the mental health team, the *Psychologist*, is the expert on testing. Historically he has been responsible for measuring intelligence, personality and psychopathology with objective and projective tests. In crisis work the testing function, especially personality testing, is used less often than clinical skills. The full battery of personality tests takes many hours for administration and report. Additionally the personality characteristics are (by definition) unlikely to change at a time of crisis. Instead of personality variables the psychologist may be asked to do very brief testing. The clinician may be interested in the presence or absence of organic brain disease, an estimate of intelligence or brief measures of the symptoms. At a time of crisis the changes are so rapid that there is little use for cross-sectional measures.

In clinical research such as the Family Treatment Unit has carried out, it was essential that baseline measures be obtained. Therefore there was an emphasis on individual and family tests of functioning. Hopefully psychologists will develop other short and simple tests which can be of help to the clinical team.

The psychologist brings to the clinical operation his own skills as a clinician plus his tradition of "evaluation." The evaluator is a researcher and psychometrician. In the past the clinicians generally would consult a psychologist if research were to be included in a treatment setting. Today, however, psychiatrists social workers and nurses are all given some research training during their professional education. The social worker or nurse who obtain doctoral degrees (and increasing numbers do) must do a major research project. He thereby obtains the same training in research given other doctoral candidates. Research is another example of the role expansion seen in all mental health professions. As the psychologist has expanded his clinical skills, the professions of medicine, social work and nursing have become more expert in research and testing.

Although the psychologist on most clinical teams has generally been a clinical psychologist, one can argue that these functions could be performed by a social psychologist equally well. In fact, a large, complex unit such as a community mental health center might well function with psychologists of several orientations. Provided that the social psychologist either comes equipped with clinical experience or acquires it in working with a clinical team, his orientation to group and family phenomena and to interaction (as well as to internalized conflict) can offer a unique contribution.

The *Social Worker* also comes from a clinical background and a variety of skills from diverse settings. His special expertise, however, has to do with social agencies. Be it a family service agency, a court, a school system or any one of many other possibilities, the social worker is generally accustomed to dealings with such agencies. In the usual clinical setting, the caseworker may find himself not only doing individual or group psychotherapy (case work is a euphemism for psychotherapy), but he will also find himself involved in getting information from these agencies, arranging for inter-agency contacts when a family has had dealings with half dozen or more of them, or participating in discharge planning which may involve the services of one of these other agencies. Generally he is the most knowledgeable member of the team about other social agencies. His basic community and "social" orientation has led him into this area.

In a populated area such as the Denver Metropolitan Area, there are literally hundreds of such facilities. To know about the functioning of many of them is a major task for a caseworker. Yet this is the particular specialized field of the social worker. Although any of the other team members may well have contact with other agencies either for information or to make a referral for services, it is generally the social worker who is called upon for this. He may also be a consultant in this specialized field.

In describing the social worker we have used the male gender. This was done because the team social worker of the Family Treatment Unit was a man. For the *nurse* the female gender will apply almost all the time. Very few men are nurses nowadays.

The particular role of the nurse, however, does not depend so much on her gender as on her public health background. Nurses with public health preparation bring a community orientation and focus to the mental health team. Public health people have been concerned with prevention, early case detection, and rehabilitation and they have been accustomed to doing this out in the field. It is the public health group which is more often found away from their own offices, clinic or hospital. Many contacts between public health personnel and individuals or families in the community have been at times of crisis. They may have occurred around the illness (contagious) or developmental period such as when the child is beginning school. Public health nurses have been found at work in industry, in schools and in homes. The visiting nurse has had a great deal of experience in dealing with a family in its home setting. It is therefore inevitable that the nurse with such a background is the team expert on making home visits. Home visits do not necessarily have to be performed by the nurse but if she does

not do the visiting herself, she has the responsibility of teaching
other team members this technic. Of great help to the other professionals is the visiting nurse's orientation toward going out to the
patient rather than waiting in an office for the patient to come in.
One other aspect of this particular area of specialization is that
visiting nurses in the community (who are not members of the
mental health crisis team) are extremely useful resources and
allies. The nurse's knowledge of community nursing resources
has enabled our team to refer approximately 20 per cent of the
families seen to public health visiting nurse services. Whether
the home visits are performed by the nurse on the team or by a
visiting nurse in the community, the contact in the home often
turns out to be valuable. Later in this chapter we have devoted
an entire section to this particular technic and its special value.

The nurse has other areas of specialization. She knows much
about medication and side effects and she can serve as an extension
of the physician in this area. It is a nurse in the hospital who
organizes the therapeutic milieu. She is well equipped to help
establish a therapeutic milieu in the home.

IMMEDIATE ISSUES AND CHRONIC PROBLEMS

One of the requirements of emergency treatment is the ability
to resolve the acute crisis while understanding and appreciating
both the influence and the chronicity of the long-term problems.
Simply, when a patient comes in with an acute dissociative reaction,
he may not be seeking treatment for his impotency or his severe
passivity, though the passivity may well influence the course of
therapy.

The therapist must keep in mind what he is treating, and remember that he is hired by the patient to treat him, not to study him or
to change his life, unless so specified. It is undoubtedly the therapist's right, even responsibility, to encourage the patient to seek
treatment for chronic problems, but the decision is the patient's.
The eagerness of psychiatrists to treat long-standing problems has
been a frequent source of conflict. Disturbingly few people really
want to change.

Chronic conflicts, character disorders, and long-standing symptoms may muddy the picture, but clearing them away must be post-

poned. Crisis therapy cannot effectively deal with chronic issues. Character traits or symptoms which receive much attention during a family fight may be needed and supported by the family between rounds.

The psychiatrist's job at this point is to know what to treat. Just because something moves is no reason for a hunter to shoot it, and just because a piece of behavior is "abnormal" is no reason for a therapist to treat it. The therapist should understand and explore the chronic issues, but attempt to change only the immediate sources of conflict. Hopefully the family will want to go for further treatment of chronic problems, but that is their decision. It should be kept in mind that there must be good reasons why people have tolerated one another through the years and these good reasons will reemerge when the crisis passes.

THE EXECUTIVE FUNCTION IN CRISIS THERAPY

The mental health professions attract people who are nondirective. It has been shown that psychiatry attracts the least authoritarian medical students. The inactive role of psychotherapist (which originates in the psychoanalytic model of therapy) is useful for regression-promoting treatment, but in crisis therapy, regression is to be avoided rather than sought. In the treatment of a crisis, the activity of the emergency room physician is helpful. A psychoanalytic technic is out of place. What the patient and family need is a respected professonal who will step in, take control, and be as directive as is necessary to help resolve the crisis. The activity may be compared to that of the family doctor who would arrive in the home for the delivery of a baby and give everybody some task, usually boiling water. The water served little purpose except to give the family something to do to keep them occupied, involved and calm.

The crisis can be helped by the therapist assuming the executive function for the family, but it can be prolonged by his failure to relinquish this command. At some point the therapist and the family will decide that the crisis is over, the necessary steps have been taken, and it is time for everyone to return to work. There is trouble if there is wide disparity in the perception of when the crisis is over and usual functioning can be resumed. The family therapist must reevaluate if the family wants to continue the crisis relationship when the therapist feels the crisis is over. Usually it is best for the therapist's executive role in the family to cease very quickly, within twenty-four to seventy-two hours, and the family to be encouraged to call their own plays. At that point, the therapist becomes the coach on the sidelines rather than the quarterback in the huddle.

The amount of direction for family functions will vary with the impairment of the family as a group and of its individual members. In treating a mildly neurotic outpatient, the therapist makes no decisions for the patient and avoids telling him what to do. On the other hand, when the patient is in a hospital a physician will give orders suggesting what the patient may eat, when he should be in bed and when ambulatory, and in what activities the patient should be involved at a particular time of day. At the same time, the psychiatrist treating the hospitalized patient would avoid giving advice about continuing a marriage or having an affair.

In treating patients outside the hospital the family therapist will take responsibility for certain decisions and functions (at the time of crisis) but not others. He should only take over those functions which the patient and his family can't handle. Usually a paranoid woman can cook the family dinner better than her psychiatrist could, but she needs to be told to quit drinking while on medication and to quit mailing crazy letters to the President. On the other hand, a severely depressed man can test reality without impairment and do his job fairly well, but he may need a strong outside push to get out of bed and go to work in the morning. If the family is made to be aware of the specific functions that must be temporarily filled, they can often fill them.

Such directiveness may be inappropriate with mild neurotics but it is very much a part of treatment with sicker patients. In a crisis, the family brings a psychotic member to the therapist for help, and they expect to be told what to do. The crisis therapist must give the family specific directions on how to handle those functions which they can't handle, but he must avoid telling them how to do things they can handle themselves. He may need to advise them for or against removing the patient's eye glasses or loaded shotgun to avoid their use in suicide attempts. He may need to be specific about who should and who should not return to work or school.

He may need to encourage or discourage a specific topic of conversation. He may need to warn against certain side effects of medications. But he need not advise about diet or hours of sleep or which movie the family shall see. Thus, while more overtly directive and controlling than the hospital psychiatrist, he directly controls a far smaller part of the patient's life. Clearly, the crisis family therapy team is not taking full responsibility for the patient. This responsiblity is being shared with the family. This is the major point of the whole approach.

"SYMPTOMS"

One of the easiest jobs in psychiatry is to dispel acute symptoms. This has been known since the early days of Freud. If the therapeutic goal is to discourage chronicity and produce a rapid return to usual functioning, it serves no purpose to retain symptoms. Of course, if the family issues are not resolved, symptoms may recur, so just removing the symptoms is not enough. Still, the acute symptoms are sufficiently disrupting to have brought the patient to the psychiatrist and are discomforting to the patient and his family. The symptoms perhaps served the important purpose of calling for help. We interpret the symptoms accordingly, focus immediately upon the current situation in which help is needed, and promise help in its resolution. This in itself may be sufficient to relieve the acute symptoms. But the symptoms have followed a period of building tension and painful anxiety which has had far reaching effects. The symptoms themselves have created new problems. All ramifications can't be dispelled immediately even after the problems are solved and the acute symptoms dispelled.

When the patient's anxiety is high, medication is indicated and may be useful for its pharamacologic effects as well as its symbolic value as an extension of the therapists. Acute schizophrenic symptoms are particularly responsive to a combination of heavy medication and direct interpretation. Anxiety states respond quickly to medication. Depressions respond more slowly to drugs but are perhaps the most effective symptoms in getting guilt and involvement from the family, and the depression generally clears when the desired attention is obtained, so environmental manipulation is rapidly effective. Electroshock, even when done on an outpatient basis, has manifold and well known disadvantages, but may be appropriate in a particular case, especially when the patient has responded to it before and believes it alone will help. Phobic states and hysteria seem to respond well to a combination of medication, direct interpretations, and supportive and authoritarian directives to give up the symptoms. Paranoid delusions pose a special problem. The high doses of medication required may be permissable initially but are not conducive to longer term functioning. Fortunately paranoid ideas are less disruptive and can be more easily retained than most severe symptoms. It thus becomes possible to more or less ignore them or contain them and let them disappear over several weeks as they become unnecessary. Direct challenges usually produce only denial and defensiveness, but often patients are relieved to have challenged the paranoid ideas they ambivalently hold. Interpretations may be useful for the family, but are rarely accepted by the patient. The delusions can often be isolated by appealing to the intact reality testing and helping the patient see the advantages of not talking about the delusions to anyone but the therapist.

With any diagnosis, a most important step is to convey the belief that the symptom is under the patient's control, was a useful weapon in interpersonal conflicts, became unnecessary when help arrived, and should now be given up. This can be conveyed with a gradation of attitudes from sympathetic awareness of the painfulness of the symptom and the patient's plight to an impatient demand that the patient stop this foolishness. If one attitude doesn't work, another is tried. This is an advantage of a team of interchangeable therapists. There remains the expectation that the acute symptoms will somewhat clear within the first twenty-four hours. The giving up of symptoms by the patient, who retains the unspoken right to redevelop them, is probably due less to any semihypnotic effect of the therapist, to the action of drugs, or to accuracy of any interpretations, than to a bargain being made between the patient and the therapist. The patient is willing to give up his symptoms because the therapist responds to the situation for which the patient was seeking a response and the therapist has promised to improve this situation and has already begun to do so by having the family sit down together and discuss it.

SUICIDAL AND HOMICIDAL PATIENTS

It is with the patient who may be of danger to himself or others that the matter of responsibility becomes most urgent. The therapist for neurotic outpatients assumes that the patient's responsibility for his actions is unimpaired. The likelihood of suicide or other violence is minimal. If the patient is sicker, and threatens suicide or homicide, he is often hospitalized. This danger is a very major reason for hospitalizing people. Drugs can reduce agitation and anxiety sufficiently to allow control to emerge. Meanwhile the patient may need constant reassurance that he does have control, a quite different matter from reassurance that someone else will provide control. The best people to provide this reassurance may well be the family members whose relationship with the patient is based on health, not illness. Of course, an opinion from a respected authority figure, such as a mental health worker, can be the deciding factor for the patient or relative.

The crisis therapist then has several responsibilities in the face of suicide or homicide danger. He must prevent a death or injury if possible, and he must protect the patient's ability to function independently in the future, if possible. If the therapist doubts the patient's controls, so will the patient and the suicide danger will increase, but if the therapist is confident, without being unresponsive, the patient's suicide danger will fall.

In treating families in crisis, we have treated many patients who had just attempted suicide, and many others who threatened suicide or homicide. All such behavior was seen as attempts at communication and the patient and his family were helped to communicate less destructively. The most important point is that the therapist must respond to the situation to which the patient is reacting, but must avoid rewarding the attempt itself and thereby encouraging repeated manipulative attempts.

Not all suicide attempts are manipulative gestures. We have seen one attempt made during an acute brain syndrome which had been precipitated by an atypical drug reaction. The patient was appropriately hospitalized for twelve hours in a general hospital emergency room until the temporary loss of control subsided. It was kept in mind that the bizarre suicide attempt was something about the drugs, not something about the patient, and in no way reflected on her ordinary control of her behavior.

The therapist then has the responsibility of differentiating the attempts to communicate pain and emotional loss and need from the calculated wishes to die to escape some insoluble problem. In either case, the vital issue is the thing to which the patient is reacting. Until this is understood, caution must prevail, and this caution may be ultimately damaging so the situation should be evaluated quickly. The traditional leisurely pace of psychiatric diagnosis and evaluation has no business in the treatment of suicidal patients. The professional's responsibility, above all, is to understand his patient.

MENTAL HOSPITALIZATION

In family crisis therapy, hospitalization is rigorously avoided. The treatment team must have firm convictions that almost all crises can be treated without psychatric hospitalization. It is often more convenient to hospitalize the patient, but the team must be prepared to deal with the inconvenience of twenty-four hour availability. In cases in which there is strong pressure to use the hospital from the patient, his family, or other members of the team, eventually the patient may become hospitalized. Most of the people who go into hospitals don't "need" to be hospitalized, though the hospitalization may be useful for the patient and convenient for the family and the psychiatrist. It is important to determine whether a hospitalization is for need or convenience, because the patient's whole life may be influenced by the difference.

Who "needs" hospitalization? We find that very few people need it, and these are nearly always people in whom the need has been created by prior hospitalization which was remembered as "needed." First hospitalizations should especially be avoided since this both labels the patient and sets a precedent for the handling of subsequent crises. The crisis therapist may be forced to hospitalize when the patient, the family, or other team members insist. One way a patient can insist is to refuse to give up symptoms otherwise. A useless power struggle might ensue and continue indefinitely unless the therapist finally gives in. Hospitalization, preferably for only a day or two, may then be considered when the patient or the family firmly believe that the patient will not give up his symptoms until he is hospitalized. We have never seen such an attitude without a history of prior hospitalization. A situation such as this, in which the hospital is endowed with magical curative powers by the patient, the family, or the doctor may be the only situation in which an alternative setting for treatment cannot be effective. An alternative setting may be less convenient for various of the involved parties, and if hospitalization is chosen, it should be clarified to all concerned that it is for *convenience*, not need.

If the hospital is to be avoided and there are reasons for avoiding the home as a treatment site also, alternatives must be found. The home may be destructive and unsuitable. It should be kept in mind though that a chaotic home situation, which would be intolerable for the psychiatrist, may be familiar and even quite comforting to the patient. Rather minor changes in a familiar atmosphere may be sufficient to produce dramatic changes in the patient's symptoms. In our experience, attempts to permanently separate people who have a long history of destructiveness to one another almost invariably fail. We have found that the surest way of getting people back together and out of treatment is to ally ourselves with the part of the patient's ambivalence which supports separation. Battling spouses or unemancipated children are unlikely to resolve their chronic problems during a crisis, and even less likely to break up, though they may scream loudly their intentions to do so. If a long-term separation seems in order, the participants should be encouraged to carefully formulate suitable plans. In either case, a brief separation may be useful in selected situations. This amounts to brief separate vacations, and a hotel may be a more appropriate setting than a hospital. One battling couple, desiring a brief separation, solved the issue by taking turns spending the night in the backyard trailer. Often there is a convenient relative or friend with a vacant bed or room. Such arrangements can provide varying degrees of needed supervision or structure. Boarding houses might be useful in some such cases. When more structure or supervision is needed, a half-way house would be useful.

The most frequently used alternative to home or psychiatric hospital is the general hospital. In an occasional case, several days in a general hospital can provide rest, a setting for psychotherapy and pharmacotherapy, and treatment for organic conditions which are related or contributory to the psychiatric problem, without adding the stigma and slow pace of the psychiatric hospital. More commonly, we have used twenty-four hour holding beds in the general hospital emergency room.[4] If the patient is out of control, combative and unmanageable, actively suicidal or homicidal, he can usually be brought under control with drugs in a few hours. Few patients have remained unmanageable after eight hours of sleep (which means rest for the family also), possibly an injection of amytal, several doses of a phenothiazine, and two or three hours of family therapy. Twenty-four hours of this approach is usually sufficient to calm and bring under control even the most severely psychotic or acutely ill patients or to dispel severe acute symptoms in the course of a more chronic illness. The emergency room atmosphere seems a more appropriate setting for this sort of therapy than the leisurely psychiatric hospital. The emergency room pace is rapid, with the expectation of symptom relief within hours rather than weeks. Fortunately for treating acute symptoms, there is nothing leisurely, protective, or tolerant about a general hospital emergency room. The nurses are efficient and tough, trained to consider psychiatric patients as people who are doing irritating or self-destructive things. In such an atmosphere, a patient is under great pressure to give up his symptoms quickly and usually does so.

The therapist must make the decision of whether to send the patient home or to find an alternative place for him to live temporarily, or to postpone the decision until the air clears by hospitalization in the emergency room overnight. This is rarely a difficult decision unless for some reason the family cannot be directly evaluated. We find that many patients insist that their families are uncaring or unbending, would be totally uncooperative, and would neither understand nor respond to the seemingly impossible conflicts. After an hour or two with the family, or even a telephone call, and some discussion of the issues, the patient finds the family surprisingly easy to live and work with. Only if the family is unresponsive or unavailable, or if the patient is making a serious and realistic effort at emancipation, do we consider an alternative living arrangement. The emergency room is used when the patient is too acutely ill to go home, until medication can take effect, when the situation just can't be evaluated quickly enough, or in such special situations as after a suicide attempt with pills whose effects can't be predicted for several hours.

THERAPEUTIC ALLIANCE

Another problem facing the treatment team is to resolve the acute problems while maintaining a positive relationship that will insure the family's readiness to return in future crises and to use the family treatment team as they do their family doctor. This is difficult for the therapist who identifies with the patient as a victim of his family. That is rarely, if ever, an accurate picture of the situation and even if it were, it can't be approached that way. The family therapist tries to make the negotiating or combatant family members more equal adversaries while emphasizing and broadening the areas of agreement. The therapist's neutrality is usually necessary and is easy to maintain if the family relationships are symmetrical, but here there is no symmetricality; the family holds power over the patient, and the therapist must to some extent be the patient's advocate in return for the patient giving up his symptoms. The therapist is too direct to be effectively neutral. The therapist is then in a tight situation which may be best resolved by studied respect for the standing rules of the family, which have previously worked to some degree. Particularly, he must recognize who holds the power in the family and avoid challenging that, while still directing traffic in the family and providing temporary reality testing. The family therapist usually avoids trouble by never challenging anyone's motives, supporting the idea that all have the best of intentions, and interpreting most problems as due to disorders of communication. This is not always possible. The best solution may be to use a team of at least two therapists who can check and counterbalance each other's tendencies to be too supportive to one member or too attacking with another. The therapist is not just an observer but temporarily becomes an active member of the family and as such, has strong emotions which are extremely useful in reality testing and evaluation, but only if carefully controlled. The therapist's reactions can get out of hand. It is often helpful for the therapists to stop the interview and review their feelings. At times, one therapist must withdraw completely. The "counter-transference" problems have nearly always arisen when the therapist expected, or even demanded, that one family member see the present situation as a crisis requiring action. Often the relative had been through this situation many times before and appropriately did not feel an immediate change in his behavior was necessary. In effect, the therapist confused an acute symptom requiring rapid resolution with a chronic exacerbated symptom to which the family was fairly well adjusted and even rewarding. At other times, problems have arisen when the family therapist insisted that a relative take more responsibility for his contribution to the patient's symptoms than previous professional contacts have attempted. A relative's appropriate guilt may be used as motivation for therapy, but attempts to produce it or uncover it when denied often fail with a nonpatient. The wishes of the relatives must be respected. If the patient can't tolerate the results, he can regain his symptoms and provide pain to motivate the family.

If the family therapist intrudes too far into the family's long-term patterns, the family may terminate the relationship and avoid future contacts. When the crisis is over, the therapists must relinquish the initial executive role, and with an emphasis on healthy functioning become family advisors who are available when needed, but not intrusive, giving advice when asked, but not working toward undesired changes. The nature of the subsequent relationship is partially dependent upon what the family finds comfortable. When the family continues to expect more than can be given, it may be because there was so much concern with keeping the "transference" positive that the family was in effect seduced. We don't expect families to enjoy contacts with us when they don't need us. We may be a painful reminder of past problems.

REFERRALS

Prompt and effective psychiatric intervention can often prevent an acute psychiatric illness from developing into a chronically disabling problem. Individuals are now being helped to more quickly resume their everyday roles and responsibilities with a minimal amount of personal and family regression. Many of the patients and families, however, are saddled with a variety of problems—vocational, financial, child-care, marital, etc.—that need help beyond crisis intervention. The frustration over years of failure to resolve these problems has left a residue of feeling which then may reach an emotional pitch which contributes to the decompensation of one family member. Therefore, once the patient has recompensated, the referral process and consideration of the next steps to be taken becomes a very significant aspect of the crisis intervention.

A large number of patients are referred for hospitalization by a variety of community resources—welfare department, minister, family physician, etc. The referring community resource currently active with the patient often provides the Family Treatment Unit with valuable diagnostic and treatment information. Time is of the essence in emergency treatment, and the more quickly one can become familiar with the patient and the family, the more quickly can the crisis be treated. Sometimes, this is facilitated by the agency representative accompanying the patient to the emergency room and in these instances, the Family Treatment Unit has had this person sit in during the interview with the patient and family.

Mrs. Kelly was accompanied to the hospital by her juvenile parole officer who had known her for several years and had a good relationship with the patient. Mrs. Kelly had a long history of foster home placements, petty stealing, and sexual promiscuity. She had recently been picked up by the police for shoplifting. When brought before the judge, Mrs. Kelly claimed that she had wanted to injure her infant child. Thereupon, the judge referred her to the hospital for psychiatric evaluation. Based on information from the juvenile parole officer and office and home visits with the Kelly family, it was obvious that the claim of wanting to injure her child was a manipulative gesture by Mrs. Kelly to avoid facing the charge of shop lifting. This information was passed on to the court and the juvenile parole officer who now had a better understanding of Mrs. Kelly's manipulation.

As a result of this immediate involvement with the referring agencies, the Family Treatment Unit has become aware of what we call the Caretaker Crisis (see Chapter VI). This is a crisis where there has been no significant change in the life situation of the patient. Instead, the agency becomes unduly anxious and alarmed about the patient and makes a referral for hospitalization. Changes in agency personnel or policy may alter the relationship the patient has with the agency. Sometimes, the therapist's difficulties with the patient may promote a referral for hospitalization.

Mrs. Moon was seen in the Adult Outpatient Clinic by a psychiatrist who felt very uncomfortable with her and was getting no place with her in therapy. There was a series of broken appointments and when Mrs. Moon decided to resume therapy, the psychiatrist did not schedule her for several weeks. Mrs. Moon felt the need to be seen quickly and the psychiatrist referred her to the Emergency Room where hospitalization was recommended. It was apparent after the Family Treatment Unit spoke with the patient and the clinic psychiatrist that the difficulty of getting an appointment with the therapist was the most immediate problem. This is not only an example of a Caretaker Crisis, but an illustration of how information gained from the referral source provides a quick assessment of what crisis needs to be treated. Thereupon, arrangements were made for Mrs. Moon to be treated by another clinic staff member.

The task in these situations is not only to work with the patient but with the referring agency to see what can be done immediately with the crisis. Agencies despair and feel unable to continue seeing certain patients. When this happens, they often will try to avoid the patient by a referral for hospitalization. Agency staffs need frequent boosting and encouragement. When this is not forthcoming with a frustrating patient, they will tend to reject and isolate the patient.

The contact with the previously involved agency does more than provide valuable information about the patient. When the referring agency has any sense of commitment to the patient, one can help continue this relationship. The immediate involvement of the other agency may insure the continuing work with the patient; it also provides the opportunity to explore alternative plans. Sometimes the referring agency is fed up with the patient. To involve them in anything more than information gathering would do harm to the patient. In such a case, it is well to evaluate the experiences the referring agency had with the patient. This material can be helpful in deciding whether or not to refer the patient elsewhere and what kind of referral should be made.

Mrs. George was referred by a private mental health clinic for hospitalization because of depression and thoughts of killing her child. The referring clinic had been seeing the Georges for about a year and was frustrated over the poor progress made with the couple. Following the crisis intervention, it was apparent that the Georges needed continuing marital counseling. The referring agency felt very hopeless about the situation, and it was thought unwise to refer them back to the clinic. Consequently, the couple were referred to a private marriage counselor. This worked out very well. The referring agency did not care to be involved in any future treatment and to have forced the couple on them would have been disastrous to all.

The involvement of community agencies is fascinating and complicated. Often there are a host of agencies involved with a patient and his family with very little communication and coordination among these different agencies. The problem in these cases may stem more from each agency imposing its goals on the family, which may serve to confuse or permit manipulation by the family. Patients and families in this multiproblem group are very appealing to community agencies because they are susceptible to many problems and appear so helpless. The tendency is for the community to take over the operations of these families, negating whatever strengths lie within them for growth and self help. The Family Treatment Unit has found that the acute psychiatric problems are often an outgrowth of the duplication of services and poor coordination of these community agencies. Once the acute psychiatric problem is handled, then the Family Treatment Unit, where indicated, will try to unravel the network of community involvement so that these different agencies more appropriately serve the family.

Community agencies unfamiliar with the acutely upset patients may become unduly frightened and refer them too hastily for psychiatric hospitalization. This only serves to intensify the individual's problems and to confirm the label "mental patient." The major task in these situations is not so much to help the patient, but to allay the concerns of the referring agency. Many psychotic breakdowns are self-limited periods of psychologic decompensation, if community agencies can be helped to stay with individuals through their periods of acute upset.

Considerations Regarding Referral

Once the Family Treatment Unit completes the crisis intervention and the patient has been restored to a pre-crisis level of functioning, an assessment needs to be made of the next steps. This assessment needs to consider the following issues: (1) What are the indications in the patient's and family's situation for and against continuing treatment and service with a community resource? (2) Where in the community should the referral be made? (3) How should an effective referral be made? (4) What is the continuing responsibility of the Family Treatment Unit to the patient and the referral resource?

Referrals that are meant to deal with long-term patterns of family interaction have to be carefully considered. Some families have been made a lot worse by receiving service for certain chronic patterns of interaction. Some family balances, deviant as they may be, are best left alone.

Mr. Peters, thirty five, had a history of five psychiatric hospitalizations and consistent unemployment during the past seven years. Mrs. Peters was very satisfied with her husband's poor functioning. She was receiving training as a licensed practical nurse under a federal plan which designated her as head of the household. Pursuant to our referral, Mr. Peters became successfully involved in a work-training program through the Department of Vocational Rehabilitation. Mrs. Peters, in turn, became depressed over her husband's improved attitude towards work and began to do poorly in her training program. She threatened to break up the marriage and attempted suicide. Finally, after putting so much pressure on her husband that he discontinued his vocational rehabilitation program, Mrs. Peters' depression lifted and her school performance improved. Essentially, the couple's marital balance was based on the husband's occasional psychiatric hospitalizations and homebound role, while the wife worked to support the family.

Referral is a broad term and sometimes all that is necessary is to give the name and address of an employment agency or a nursing home. There was one situation in which a women was caring for her aged and senile mother. At times she got fed up in caring for the mother and wanted to place her in a nursing home. However, she was not emotionally prepared to make a nursing home placement, but instead, wanted to threaten the mother so as to get her to cooperate more at home. The woman did get some satisfaction out of going through the motions of contacting the nursing home.

She gained some momentary relief and the mother's behavior improved under the threat of going to a nursing home. Six months later, the woman felt more comfortable about placing her mother in a nursing home.

The Family Treatment Unit, having developed an understanding of a patient's background and personality, may decide that a particular referral would encourage regression and dependency.

Mr. Ames, thirty three, had a very poor work history, shifting from one job to another. Throughout his ten years' of marriage he continued to be supported by his parents. Mr. Ames had a year and a half of outpatient psychotherapy with no substantial improvement in his behavior. He blamed his failure on his hatred of his father who had never given him the necessary emotional support through the growing-up years. At the time, the Family Treatment Unit felt that to refer Mr. Ames for Vocational Rehabilitation would only promote more irresponsible functioning as he had the necessary intellect and ability to do sales work. He did finally begin to work regularly after we met with his parents and pointed out how their continued financial support was damaging his motivation for work and financial independence.

There are other situations in which there is a need for continuing treatment, but at termination of the crisis intervention, the individual does not want to follow through with any referral. However, when the patient comes back to the Family Treatment Unit for help with subsequent crises, he then appears more disposed towards accepting a referral.

Mr. Temple was treated for depression after making a serious suicide attempt. He had many long-standing psychological problems which were affecting his job performance and marriage. Regular psychotherapy treatment was felt to be advantageous. However, he did not accept a referral initially as he wanted to handle these matters on his own. After returning to the Family Treatment Unit several times because of subsequent episodes of depression, outpatient psychotherapy was arranged.

In general, the Family Treatment Unit has found that whenever we have to get "pushy" with a patient or family about referral, then we may as well back off. Though not disposed to accepting a referral initially, they may be willing to accept it later on. It is wise not to get too invested in a referral early as it then may make it more difficult for the patient and family to return in times of subsequent crises. Referral, therefore, is a mutual process between the crisis team and the patient; and though the professional may feel that he knows more about what needs to be done, careful consideration has to be given to how the family feels about it. In the long run, it is the family who has to make use of the referral source.

The Family Treatment Unit referred about fifty per cent of the patients and families to community resources. There has been varying success in meeting the goals of referral. Public Health Nurses are particularly effective with patients needing continuing supervision of their medication and other medical problems. Through regular home visits, visiting nurses can help families with problems of household management and child care. The public health nurses have appropriately reinvolved the Family Treatment Unit whenever they have encountered unmanageable subsequent crisis with the families. Patients with serious employment problems because of emotional and social impairment and lack of marketable work skills have, in many situations, been helped by the local Department of Vocational Rehabilitation. Of all the community resources however, it seems that private physicians, general practitioners and psychiatrists, and community mental health clinics are the most difficult to work with in coordinating efforts with the patient and family. What customarily happens is that the patient and family go for several sessions and discontinue. These continuing resources feel that they have done all they can and the patient and family are no longer motivated for treatment. They do not notify the Family Treatment Unit as to the outcome with the patient and the family. The theme of the clinic and the private physician is "you are my patient and I will stay with you as long as you are motivated and cooperative. When you stop coming to see me, my responsibility ends."

Referral Process

The referral should be a live process and not a mere formality such as writing a letter and giving a name and address to the patient. The Family Treatment Unit has tried to make the referral a more vital process by going outside our office and meeting the patient and family at the community agency. The Family Treatment Unit also makes itself available to the resource for continuing consultation in any future crisis with the patient. This hopefully creates an ongoing working relationship with the referral agency in which they will feel less overwhelmed with difficult and anxiety provoking psychiatric patients. In making a referral, the Family Treatment Unit has learned to be very careful not to dictate to the community agency what should be done with a patient and family. This kind of overinvolvement may be an outgrowth of our relationship with the patient during crisis treatment. We may have something in mind for the patient which the other agency cannot offer. Community resources can only approximate our goals for the patient. Agencies have their own guide rules and we have learned that we must respect them if we are to work with them.

Sometimes despite the Family Treatment Unit's best efforts at referral, the patient will come back dissatisfied. Though we possibly may have made the wrong referral, on further exploration we may find the patient is unable to separate. During crisis treatment, the professionals and the patients establish strong alliances which both parties are reluctant to relinquish once the crisis intervention is over. When this happens, the Family Treatment Unit works rapidly on the separation problem and immediately returns the family or patient to the community agency.

The Family Treatment Unit is available for further consultation and expeditious rehandling of the referred patients. Community agencies are very relieved when we continue to share the responsibility for the patient and the family during times of future crises. Traditionally, there is a dichotomy between the crisis intervention and ongoing contact. Once a referral has been made, emergency treatment units often break off contact. The Family Treatment Unit's continuing availability sets up an immediate rapport, and community agencies are more prone to accept psychiatric cases. They are otherwise frightened of psychiatric patients and steer clear of them, but this close liaison helps to offset this fear.

Through this close relationship with community agencies, we have become aware of their need for encouragement to work with demanding psychiatric patients and families. Agencies and their personnel may become very frustrated and sometimes will reject the patient. These cases have come to our attention again when former patients appear in the emergency room ready for hospitalization. However, if the relationship with the community agency is a good one they will contact us when beginning to experience difficulty with the patient.

Once a referral is made, the Family Treatment Unit has learned not to expect the other agency to carry the patient and family indefinitely. When the community agency has attained its goals with the patient and family, it will appropriately discharge them.

In summary, the experience of the Family Treatment Unit has been that to be effective, an emergency psychiatric service has to maintain a close liason with community agencies. As more than fifty per cent of the patients seen by the Family Treatment Unit have been referred, the continuing value of what is achieved in crisis treatment will depend on the work of the community agencies. The referral process is just as important to the operation of the Family Treatment Unit as the direct work with patients and families.

HOME VISITS

Home visits were originally felt to be the special skill of the nurse because of her public health background. However, social workers in welfare settings and physicians from general practice also have a background in visiting the homes of patients. The other mental health professions have come to realize the value of seeing the patient and family in their own setting.

Much of the clinical work presented in this book was worked out by trial and error in its initial phases. Our current model is a direct result of experience in the home. One error we made early in the project was to try to turn the home into a hospital. This was particularly evident in families with a "chronic" patient. Inevitably the family would rebel against its unwanted social worker, nurse, and doctor role and would maneuver in such a way as to make it too difficult to try to prevent the hospitalization. The hospitalization, which was what the family desired in the first place, would result much to the disgruntlement of the treatment team. The team would be disgruntled because there were probably multiple home visits aimed at supporting the family efforts, and much involvement and failure, at least as defined by the treatment team, was the result.

The current design is to visit the family in the home within twenty-four hours of admission to the project. This is usually the team's only contact in the home. A clinical team would have difficulty operating exclusively in the home and carrying a reasonable service load too. However, it might be feasible for some teams operating exclusively in the home if there is enough manpower and if communications among team members are good. The relationship developed with the team that is comfortable in the home setting facilitates ease in effecting a positive working alliance with the family. This is important to develop quickly not only in a crisis operation, but in many of the clinical settings where the patient and his family are not candidates for long-term therapy.

Home visiting has proven to be a highly desirable tool in crisis assessment. It adds another part to the sorting out of a frequently puzzling situation. The situation of a family that is living in a neighborhood and home beyond their current financial resources is best understood by acquainting oneself with the actual circumstances. The family who desires that mother be hospitalized because she no longer does the household chores but occupies her bed instead may best be treated where the presenting problem exists. The mother assigned the task of cleaning her kitchen can less often block the therapist's pressure if he is aware of the dimension of the task. Reality is seen and dealt with in its proper perspective.

The things to be observed in any home visit are the kind of neighborhood and house the family lives in. More specifically, is the neighborhood a heterogenous or homogenous one, are the lawns and yards cared for, are there churches, schools, or industries present? Does the family seem to fit in with the style of the neighborhood or are they a poor fit? During the home visit it is hoped that all family members are present. This enables the discerning person to observe the family's interaction with one another. One should be cautioned to remember to look at strengths as well as weakness. This is something that can be supported and rewarded. The home is an excellent medium for learning how parents discipline children as well as how parents discipline each other.

When daily living experiences in the home situation become a problem, they are often treated in the home, usually by the nurse. One family who was seen by the Family Treatment Unit presented as its main problem a young mother who ceased to manage her household and children. For two years, since the birth of her child,

she had become used to the exhilarating effects of the ampheta-
mines. Her difficulty began several months before when her private
physician discontinued her supply of medicines. The patient had
come to feel she could not do any household chores without the
drug's assistance. She became depressed and was hospitalized for
one month where she received electroshock treatments. At home
she continued her nonfunctioning and became more and more depressed. She was brought to the emergency room by her husband
and mother-in-law after she threatened suicide. The members of
the Family Treatment Unit saw the "patient," her husband, and
mother-in-law. There was much competition between the two
women with the younger often the loser. The mother-in-law was a
compulsively neat housekeeper and a striving business woman. Her
son was closely attached to her. The patient repeatedly stated that
without her "pills" she could not keep up with her housework. She
was afraid of not being able to live up to her mother-in-law and
losing her husband. The goals of the Family Treatment Unit were
to convince the younger woman that she could perform her household duties without pills. The nurse on the team visited the patient
at home for several days in a row. Over a cup of coffee, a schedule
of housecleaning tasks was drawn up based on what the patient said
needed to be done in the household. As each task was performed
it was checked off the schedule and reviewed by the nurse and the
patient the next day. By the third day the patient was beginning
to express confidence in her ability to perform as a wife and a
mother. The youngest child who had been staying with his grandmother was returned home. Conjoint family therapy was carried
on at the same time and the competition between the women was
discussed and the husband helped to align himself with his wife.
The nurse, in joint meetings as well as in the home, was able to
realistically support the young woman's functioning. Having the
Family Treatment Unit team as her ally enabled the young woman
to feel confident in her own resources without the assistance of pills.

THE SEX OF THE FAMILY THERAPIST

Being a woman on an interdisciplinary team has its rewards and
its problems. Professional women today are confronted with the
double-edged sword of trying to appear essentially nonaggressive,

yet are expected to be creative and innovative. A certain degree of conflict with male team members is bound to occur.

From a therapeutic standpoint, the female therapist has many advantages along with or apart from male therapists in family treatment settings. As a reality confronter, the role both as professional person and a woman in the home situation has already been mentioned. In the office too the sex of the therapist may be important. It may be worthwhile to have co-therapists of opposite sexes, and a woman can use individual situations to help understand and work with family problems.

Exemplary of the former situation is the treatment technic of showing a husband and wife a visual demonstration of their interaction by the male and the female therapist assuming the couples' roles to show their interaction. This may also be used as a medium for showing a couple how to better relate to one another. The couple in which the woman continually interrupts her husband's explanations can be humorously yet poignantly portrayed by the male and female therapist and then corrected for the benefit of the couple. The female therapist may also be more perceptive and empathic toward a distraught member of her own sex.

Rather than take a therapeutic stand of rigidly adhering to one form of treatment, the Family Treatment Unit has found that occasionally seeing people apart from their families is desirable. Teenagers seem to need to have a relationship with a member of their own sex who is not involved in the home situation. This a woman member of the team can provide on a crisis basis. This relationship may help in determining to whom to refer the patient for longer term help. The female school counselor may be the best possible referral for many school girls who are faced with the dilemma of emancipating from their role as a child in the family and emerging as an adult member of society; likewise a male school counselor may serve the same function for a teenage boy.

DRUG THERAPY

The tranquilizers, energizers and sedatives are important aids in family crisis therapy. In the Family Treatment Unit's 150 families, more than three-fourths of the nominal patients received medication. In one-fourth of the families, a member other than the "patient" also received medicine. Just as the psychoactive drugs have permitted mental hospitals to open their doors, they have also aided in avoiding hospitalization. They have been most useful in diminishing tension, in relieving psychotic symptoms, in improving depressed moods, and in helping effect sleep.

There is little that is distinctive in the use of medication by the Family Treatment Unit. The most frequently used drugs are the phenothiazines. Chlorpromazine and thioridazine were the drugs most frequently prescribed because they seemed to be more familiar and therefore more predictable and comfortable for the physicians of the team. All dosage forms have been used including injectables, oral concentrates, pills and "spansules." For the unmanageably agitated patient, who may be psychotically depressed, acutely schizophrenic, or catatonic, it may be important to produce rapid sedation. Intramuscular amytal, 3¾ gr. to 7½ gr., is more suitable for the nonpsychotic, since its duration of action is short and its side effects limited. Amytal has been useful for neurotic depressives who have not slept for several nights, for very anxious hyperventilators, and for acute anxiety attacks. For psychotic reactions, intramuscular chlorpromazine, 50 to 100 mg., has been quite dramatically effective in producing sedation and dispelling disruptive symptoms. After a few hours' sleep, patients who have received an injection of chlorpromazine may be quite cooperative and able to function in a nonpsychotic manner. It may be useful to begin oral chlorpromazine, perhaps in "spansule" form, at the time of the initial injection. The "spansules" with their prolonged action have an advantage for use with patients who might forget or refuse to take their pills if the effects of the medicine were allowed to wear off between doses. Dosages under 200 mg. a day are rarely used and the dosage has been as high as 3600 mg. a day. The usual starting dose has been 150 mg. twice a day or 75 or 100 mg. q.i.d. Chlorpromazine does have unpleasant side effects in this dosage range. For this reason, an antiparkinsonian agent is prescribed for any dosage above 400 mg. a day.

Ordinarily, the dosage is raised rapidly until the desired effect is achieved within the first few days. Then, if maintenance medication is indicated, the dosage may be reduced.

For most schizophrenic patients, it is safer to continue a moderate maintenance dosage for many months after the acute psychotic episode than to stop medication prematurely. The drugs should be discontinued only when the physician is available to observe any difficulties that arise. When a maintenance dosage is continued for many months or years in a chronic schizophrenic patient, a visiting nurse may be helpful in checking for side effects and in making sure the patient continues to take the drug. It is, of course, not necessary for the physician to see each patient on drugs each week, especially if he knows the patient and the patient can contact the physician if some need arises.

Thioridazine is quite similar to chlorpromazine. It may be just as effective in doses below 800 mg. a day and has far fewer side effects. It may be more sedating in higher doses. The oral concentrate is only a little slower in onset than injectable chlorpromazine, but giving about 300 mg. of concentrate in a glass of orange juice requires the cooperation of the patient who may object to the taste and finish drinking with an indefinite amount inside him and the rest on the walls. We would not try to disguise it, since this might impair the subsequent relationship. After the patient is under control with chlorpromazine, he may be switched to thoridazine for more comfortable maintenance.

The only other phenothiazine used by the F.T.U. is trifluoperozine. This drug produces frequent severe extrapyramidal reactions, but is less sedating than chlorpromazine or thioridazine. It is useful in doses of 20 to 40 mg. a day for patients who must remain alert on their jobs, yet require high doses of phenothiazines. It also has been used in combination with chlorpromazine to minimize the side effects of both.

In milder situations, which might call for lower doses of phenothiazines, the minor tranquilizers have often been used. Chlordiazepoxide and diazepam seem almost interchangeable and, in practice, have little effect beyond mild sedation. Unlike the phenothiazines, they are not unpleasant to take and may be addicting. During a crisis, they might calm a relative as well as indicate that he too was involved in the crisis. These drugs might serve as soothing extensions of the therapists. They might also alleviate the sort of everyday anxieties which would otherwise be drowned in alcohol or acted out in a family fight or a new symptom. Perhaps they are best reserved for p.r.n. use by people with low anxiety tolerance, such as alcoholics, hyperventilators, mild depressives, and retired people who are bored at times. An occasional patient, usually chronically depressed and inactive, may not be able to sleep without help, but sex and exercise seem to be better than sleeping pills for most patients, so the use of barbiturates for sleep has been fairly limited.

For psychotic depressives, imipramine in dosages of 100 to 150 mg. a day can be effective. Desimipramine has not been noted to be more rapid. These drugs, and others which are similar but not necessarily any better, are slow to act and if the patient is agitated, phenothiazine sedation may be indicated for the first week or two. Neurotic depressions, which may be merely an emotional lability and intolerance to anxiety, rarely respond to imipramine, but may be soothed by diazepam until the issues can be resolved. Only rarely is a stimulant used. Ritaline, once in the morning, may activate a bored elderly person as something a bit stronger than a few cups of breakfast coffee. Stronger stimulants have been avoided.

Many of the indications for the minor tranquilizers, stimulants, hypnotics, or even antidepressives are actually scheduling problems. With reasonable activity, satisfying sexual release, the judicious intake of caffeine, and regular hours, most of these drugs are no longer needed.

Bibliography

1. Bardill, Donald R. and Bevilacqua, Joseph J. Family interviewing by two caseworkers. Social Casework. 45:278-282, 1964.

2. Becker, Alvin and Weiner, Leonard. Psychiatric home treatment service: community aspects. In: Masserman, Jules (Ed.): Current Psychiatric Therapies. Vol. VI, New York: Grune & Stratton, 1966.

3. Framo, James L. Rationale and techniques of intensive family therapy. In: Boszormenyi-Nagy, Ivan and Framo, James L. (Eds.): Intensive Family Therapy. New York: Harper & Row, 1965.

4. Kritzer, Herbert and Pittman, Frank S. Twenty-four hour hospitalization in a general emergency room setting. Hosp. Community Psychiat. In Press.

5. MacGregor, Robert et al. Multiple Impact Therapy with Families. New York: McGraw-Hill, 1964.

6. Rubenstein, David and Weiner, Oscar R. Co-therapy teamwork relationships in family psychotherapy. In: Zuk, Gerald H. and Boszormenyi-Nagy, Ivan (Eds.): Family Therapy and Disturbed Families. Palo Alto: Science & Behavior Books, 1967.

7. Sonne, John C. and Lincoln, Geraldine. Heterosexual co-therapy team experiences during family therapy. Family Process. 4:177-97, 1965.

8. Wynne, Lyman C. Some indications and contraindications for exploratory family therapy. In: Boszormenyi-Nagy, Ivan and Framo, James L. (Eds.): Intensive Family Therapy. New York: Harper & Row, 1965.

CHAPTER 4

A Crisis of Marital Separation

Marital conflict is a major concern of all family therapy. Even when the problem for which help is sought is defined as an individual one, when the family is seen, interactional conflict is surprisingly apparent. Among the cases seen by the Family Treatment Unit, two thirds of the identified patients were married and lived with their spouses. In about sixty per cent of these marriages, divorce was being openly contemplated, threatened, or feared at the time of the initial interview. Another five per cent had just undergone a dissolution of their marriages. In other words, two thirds of the married identified patients had just faced, or were currently facing the possibility of separation or divorce. This would seem to be an extraordinarily high degree of serious marital discord.

There are several possible explanations for the shakiness of these marriages: (1) It might be assumed that the identified patient's fear of divorce could be a symptom arising from guilt over some real or imagined failure. Actually, in only one case was the identified patient's fear unconfirmed when the spouse was confronted with it. (2) the threat of divorce might be a tactic used by the spouse to stop the offending symptomatic behavior of the identified patient. This maneuver was seen, but usually merely rationalized the spouse's desire for divorce. (3) The spouse might be exhausted by the identified patient's symptoms and might desire separation, either by divorce or hospitalization. This was often seen, but rarely in marriages which had not known previous serious conflict. (4) Most commonly, the marital conflict preceded the development of intolerable symptoms and was either a prominent stress in the crisis or a block to the resolution of the crisis.

An important part of the evaluation of the family and the identification of the crisis is the determination of the degree of marital conflict, the desire of either or both parties for divorce or separation, and the position of such desire in the sequence of events that led to the request for hospitalization. In many marriages, when a crisis of any sort occurs, the first solution considered is divorce or hospitalization, both characterized by separation, avoidance, and scapegoating. In such a crisis, it is unusual for either spouse to have made such a firm commitment to divorce that he will not consider alternatives.

The Family Treatment Unit tries to prevent such primitive solutions to crises and tries to postpone decisions about separation until the couple is freer to make a rational choice. The first step is to examine the history of the marriage and place the present crisis in historical perspective. In this process, communication is reopened. The marriage looks different when it has been reviewed and its past gratifications emphasized. The next step is to examine the solutions already attempted by the couple and find why they failed. Usually the treatment team can propose simple solutions to the immediate problems, solutions requiring minimal change in familiar patterns of behavior. These alternatives in the form of family tasks are usually accepted and no further serious consideration of divorce is made. If any long-standing dissatisfaction with the marriage persists, further negotiation of the conflicts is required. Finally, alternatives of separation versus change may have to be considered by each spouse. Those couples who desire a more gratifying marriage can be referred for long-term marriage counseling or couple's therapy. The treatment team focuses on helping the couple produce enough change to allow them to live together (or apart) without driving each other crazy.

Very few of these marriages are in actual danger of dissolution after some alternative has been presented. A few separations do occur (in our sample about ten per cent of the conflictual marriages) but most of these couples eventually get back together. When a separation is inevitable or a "fait accompli," the Family Treatment Unit's task becomes somewhat different. An effort is made to provide alternatives, but if these are rejected, the decision to separate, even if one-sided, is respected. The effort then is to make the separation as nonpunitive and as conflict-free as possible, a difficult task at best and one made near impossible by lawyers, mothers-in-law, and others whose roles are to take sides and arm for battles.

The manner in which a separation takes place is all important, as will be illustrated by the following case history. There are many ways in which a marital separation may occur. A man may be given a choice between some aspect of his behavior and continuing the marriage, or he may return home one day and discover his wife has run off with another man. The difference is enormous.

CASE HISTORY

The Family Treatment Unit had been called by the Emergency Psychiatric Service at 11:35 a.m. Dr. Cook, the resident on duty informed us that he was about to admit Mr. Wilbur Simpson to Colorado Psychopathic Hospital. Since Mr. Simpson fit the other criteria by living in an adjoining suburban county, with his sister and brother-in-law, and coming voluntarily for admission, an en- velope was opened and the family was accepted for crisis family therapy. Dr. Cook's note about Mr. Simpson read:

Mr. Simpson called Colorado General Hospital this morning and was told by someone to come to the Emergency Psychiatric Service and there was a doctor on call at all times who would see him. His wife left him about a month ago and Mr. Simpson hasn't been feeling right since.

Patient states that he feels he is "going to crack up" unless he gets some help in dealing with his feelings following his wife's having left him a month ago. She has subsequently served divorce papers on him and has issued a restraining order. He has become progressively de- pressed over the past several weeks; and, as a result, lost his job at a service station because the owner said he had too many emotional problems. He has been enrolled in an auto mechanics training school for the past two months and he speaks of being unable to continue on in training because of his inability to concentrate in that he is so pre- occupied with feelings concerning his wife, children, and the other man. He speaks of his fears that he will lose control and kill the man who took his wife from him; in addition, he speaks of what he calls "sick ideas" having to do with sexually mutilating the other man should he lose control and go after him.

Patient is generally tearful, appears and speaks in a depressed man- ner. He relates in a dependent and clinging fashion, although when he speaks of his anger towards the other man, he becomes openly enraged and gives the appearance of being brutal in terms of his con- trol. No evidence of psychotic symptomatology. He pleads for help at this point stating that he does not know if he can remain responsible for his actions.

This note was written after the patient was accepted by the Family Treatment Unit rather than being hospitalized and so it is influenced by the course of action it must justify. It thus underplays Dr. Cook's evident concern about Mr. Simpson's control of his anger and avoids mention of Dr. Cook's speculations about the severity of Mr. Simpson's paranoia.

Fear of loss of control is a common and serious symptom requiring reassurance of the patient's control and the therapist's availability and interest, as well as medication and environmental changes to reduce anxiety until the provocative situation can either be relieved or faced more calmly. With homicide as with suicide, the desire and intent of violence or death does call for outside intervention and control such as a hospital or jail may provide. The threat of suicide or homicide as a manipulative or a communicative attempt should receive response to the message underneath the threat rather than just to the content of the threat. Hospitalization is rarely necessary if the message is received and acknowledged. The expression of a fear of loss of control and resultant violence expresses a wish, probably without the intent to carry out the wish. But it also contains a message about the intensity of the sender's suffering, anger, and desperation, a message begging acknowledgment, perhaps empathy, and certainly appropriate action from the receiver. The therapist may respond with action of his own or by interpreting the message to the appropriate receiver in the patient's life. When the patient expresses a fear of loss of control, he may be asking for outside control or the reassurance that he can exert this control himself, perhaps with the therapist's help. It would be destructive to convey to the patient that he indeed lacked control over his actions and was weaker than his destructive impulses. If he really is out of control and his anxiety or impulses are truly overwhelming, or he is already out of control, an injection of phenothiazines and/or barbiturates in sufficient quantity to produce sleep has been found to restore control upon awakening in almost all cases. Our more conservative approach to the fear of loss of control is simple reassurance, anti-anxiety agents to reduce both fear and the impulses, ego reinforcement from the therapists, and the therapists' takeover of certain familial role assignments to provide controls within the family. For example, it may be suggested that loaded guns or other obvious weapons be removed from the home and some close family member stay in the house to reassure the patient until the drugs or psychotherapy can relieve the fear. The patient is told to resist the destructive impulses. He may be given specific instructions about activities to be avoided, such as drinking or a discussion of certain subjects, and others to be encouraged, such as going on to work.

Wilbur Simpson was twenty-eight years old. He was rather short and a few pounds overweight. His hair was skin colored, his complexion ruddy, his face round and chubby, and he wore glasses, all combining to make him look short, round, and unimpressive. There was grease under his broken fingernails. His clothes had not been cleaned recently, but were not old and were warm enough for the January weather. He came to the hospital with his brother-in-law, a tall, strong man of twenty-seven, who was calmly reassurring to the patient.

The immediate task was to evaluate the danger of homicide. Accordingly, Mr. Simpson and his brother-in-law were brought to the Family Treatment Unit's interviewing room and seen for about ten minutes by Mr. F. (social worker) and Dr. P. (psychiatrist). As soon as we learned that the brother-in-law was not afraid of Mr. Simpson's loss of control, we explained briefly the operation of the Family Treatment Unit, excused ourselves for lunch, and left the two men in the room to fill out various forms and questionnaires.

When we returned, we interviewed the two men for about an hour. In response to an open ended question to Mr. Simpson about his wife, he said he'd married her six years before. He'd met her a few months after he divorced his first wife for infidelity. He felt the second marriage was OK for the first two years. Then they moved to a trailer court. There they met a neighbor and first he, and then she, fell under his evil influence. From this beginning we learned much about Mr. Simpson's marriage. While in the Navy, he had married his first wife by whom he had one son. She was repeatedly unfaithful to him so he divorced her, obtained custody of the child, and left the boy for his parents to raise. Then he met his present wife. He was twenty-two, she was seventeen. She had left school in the eighth grade and had been pointed out to him as "an easy lay" by the boys at the service station where he worked. She never denied the stories. He married her, bought her a trailer, and took a job in construction. She tried to work as a cashier but couldn't make change. There were two children. Mr. Simpson recalled only a few open conflicts. A major sore spot was Mrs. Simpson's mother, who left her husband, entered a common law relationship with another man and had three children by him. Mr. Simpson tried to convince his wife this was bad and should be condemned. Mrs. Simpson resented the criticisms of her mother. Mr. Simpson recalled that his wife also complained that he wanted sex too often, didn't bathe enough, and paid her and the children too little attention.

There were two issues Mr. Simpson felt were particularly important in his wife's decision to leave. One concerned money. The couple had saved enough money for a down payment on a house. Mrs. Simpson felt cramped in the couple's trailer and wanted a house. A few months before, Mr. Simpson had invested the money in a mechanic's school training course, thus dashing her hopes for a house. The other issue was his relationship with the next door neighbor in the trailer park. The neighbor was a middle-aged divorced man with a series of young mistresses. Mr. Simpson told him all his thoughts and problems, frequently asking his advice. Mrs. Simpson had complained about their closeness.

On the night she left, Mr. Simpson was working. Mrs. Simpson brought his lunch to him at work, kissed him and left. There had been no arguments and he was surprised to return home and find his wife and children gone. The neighbor told him she'd left for good, that he had moved her out and was paying for her divorce, and that it all served him right. This was a few days after Christmas.

Since then, Mr. Simpson had made repeated efforts to contact his wife, to no avail, and had received his only communications from her through her lawyer and the neighbor. He found where she was staying and watched her window each night, interpreting what he saw as evidence that she was sleeping with the neighbor. The sister and brother-in-law also had seen her with the neighbor. When Mrs. Simpson found her husband spying on her, she took out a restraining order against him and filed for divorce on the grounds of mental cruelty. The neighbor had agreed to pay for the divorce. Mr. Simpson filed a countersuit claiming adultery with the neighbor. After that, he blamed his wife's leaving on his interest in cars, his enrollment in mechanics school and his infrequent bathing. He lost interest in school and quit going, was preoccupied at work and lost his job, became anorectic and lost twenty pounds, slept poorly, and was preoccupied with thoughts of killing the neighbor. After the divorce papers were filed, his lawyer suggested that he move out of the trailer into his sister's house. He did so. Then he visited the Emergency Psychiatric Service and obtained some imipramine, which he had been taking for two weeks. It had not helped. Now he felt he was going to lose control.

In the telling of this story, Mr. Simpson made several representative remarks about his wife and his neighbor. "She's easily influenced." "She's an old man's fool." "It's not her fault. She came under his influence." "I have no resentment toward her." "First, I thought the blame was mine, then I blamed him." "I know him. He'd never give her anything for nothing." "He was waiting for a chance to turn it to his advantage." "I put my money for school but he's offered her a house and a Cadillac." He also recognized, "If I kill him, I'll be locked up and I'll never see them." "Maybe I could just put sugar in his gas tank." "I'd like to get ahold of him and have the satisfaction of knowing that son of a bitch would never go to bed with anyone else."

The immediate goals of this initial hour were severalfold. The first purpose was to understand the symptoms and the setting in which they arose. The reality of the setting was clear. Wilbur Simpson had lost his wife, his children, and his best friend. The actual loss and the degree of adjustment required was enormous. He clearly saw the wife and children as objects, pawns in the battle between the friend-father figure and himself. The father-figure had won by offering bigger and better houses, cars, and sex. Mr. Simpson felt emasculated. At first he blamed himself and expiated by withdrawing interest from all the things in which she had resented his interest before. As this internalization became too painful, he projected his anger onto the neighbor. At no time was he aware of anger at the wife. We did not know whether this was because he had not yet appreciated the loss and experienced her only as an inanimate object, or simply because such anger would have been too threatening. There was much suggestion that he had never experienced his wife as a person and that this was a major reason for her leaving.

But even before we determined the feasibility of effecting a reconciliation, we had to decide whether we could work with the patient outside the hospital. There was no push for hospitalization from the patient or relatives, so no one had to be convinced of our approach. The crisis was obvious so we did not have to reinterpret the symptoms as communications about a crisis, rather than unintelligible craziness which had little relation to anything outside the patient's intrapsychic chaos. Still, we must consider the possible problem that the patient's symptoms would lead to danger for him or others. Our evaluation suggested that he did have control over his actions and required only minimal structure and control. This could be provided by the sister and brother-in-law and reinforced by us from a distance. We were concerned about his anger at the neighbor less because we feared that he would kill him, since a confrontation could be avoided even if the anger could not be worked out, than because the relationship between Mr. Simpson and the neighbor could not be worked out face to face. The neighbor would not be involved. So, while the meaning of this relationship might be fruitful for individual exploration, the focus for family therapy and rapid resolution of the depression must be shifted to the husband-wife relationship. Another reason for examining the marital relationships was the hope of providing Mr. Simpson awareness of what went wrong and help to prepare him for a more successful relationship in the future with the same or another woman.

For these reasons, we tried to shift the focus from the relationship with the neighbor to the relationship with the wife. We commented several times on the lack of anger at the wife and attempted to explore any fear of being angry at her. We got no response except to be reminded that every communication to him of his wife's anger and dissatisfaction had come to him through the neighbor, while his last direct contact with his wife had occurred before she left when she gave him his lunch and a kiss. Clearly, to quickly shift his anger from the neighbor to the wife and examine the marriage would require that he hear about the divorce from her, not him. Accordingly, we made the plan to contact the wife and assured Mr. Simpson we would arrange a meeting. We told him that no one had refused to see us yet (which was true at that time). We also assured him his anger (still unstated) at her was understandable and that his preoccupation with the neighbor's role could only be destructive. We then gave him the direct advice to stay away from both the wife and the neighbor. We involved the brother-in-law in maintaining this. Commenting on Mr. Simpson's unrealistic blame of his work and school for the separation, we advised him to find a job and meanwhile to return to school whether he was interested or not. We prescribed imipramine, made an appointment for the next day, and gave each man a card with telephone numbers at which we could be reached at any time.

Ordinarily we would have scheduled a home visit, but it was impossible because of the restraining order to visit the trailer and there seemed to be little need for visiting the sister's home. We would have proceeded quite differently if the sister or brother-in-law had been afraid of or angry at Mr. Simpson. In that case we would have to work more closely with the other couple to resolve the crisis in their relationship with Mr. Simpson, and a home visit would be our next step. Since there were no serious problems between Mr. Simpson and the couple, we could proceed to the provocative marital relationship.

We therefore called Mrs. Simpson to explain what was going on and to make an appointment. Mrs. Simpson said she didn't want to be involved. It was pointed out that she was already involved by the fact that she was still his wife and the mother of his children. She said she had nothing to say to him. It was pointed out that she hadn't told him why she left. She said she didn't love him anymore. She was asked to tell him that and to explain why. She was told that he was quite depressed and needed this confrontation with her. We agreed to discourage his spying on her if she would talk with him once. She said her lawyer would not let her so we agreed to discuss it with her lawyer.

We then called Mrs. Simpson's lawyer and received the remarkable message that he was not interested in Mr. Simpson's health, that he suspected this was part of a plot concocted by Mr. Simpson's lawyer, that he feared we'd try to do marriage counseling with the couple, and that it should be unethical for a doctor to interfere with a divorce. We assured him we'd had no contact with Mr.

Simpson's lawyer, that we were less concerned with patching up the marriage than with smoothly ending it, and that under no circumstances would we testify for either side. The lawyer then insisted that we promise not to get the couple back together and prevent the divorce. We did so, but he still refused to let us see Mrs. Simpson.

We then called Mr. Simpson's lawyer. He was pleased that we were taking control of Mr. Simpson since he had found the depressed man very demanding. Still he opposed a joint interview with the Simpsons, since he had fantasies of charging the neighbor with alienation of affection, and for some obscure reason, a joint interview would spoil the purity of the case.

This lawyer was somewhat less suspicious of his colleague than Mrs. Simpson's lawyer was of him, so we told him our feelings about the destructiveness of the legal battles to Mr. Simpson. We outlined our impression that his anger at the neighbor and his inability to face his feelings about the loss of the wife was due to the absence of an opportunity to see her and plead his case to her. The lawyer felt he had contributed to the overemphasis on the other man's role in his enthusiasm about the issue of alienation of affection, and recognized that a different approach was now indicated. He agreed to talk to Mrs. Simpson's lawyer and do what he could to arrange a meeting.

The second day began with a call from Mrs. Simpson's lawyer. He would not let his client be subjected to a psychiatric examination when she was not charged with any crime. After a few minutes of reassurance he agreed to a joint interview if he were allowed to be present and to stop it at any point. He again was assured that we would not testify. We asked him to clear things with the husband's lawyer for a meeting the next day.

In the afternoon, Mr. Simpson came in alone. Miss D. and Dr. P. saw him. Three therapists seems excessive for one family, let alone one member. Still we like for each family to know each team member, and vice versa, so switching therapists is not unusual. Here also, there was the feeling that a female therapist would help counteract the specific loss. As it turned out, little rapport could be established, so Mr. F. returned for subsequent interviews at Miss D.'s request.

Mr. Simpson had brought a letter from his wife. We read it. The letter was angry, hastily written and poorly spelled, but clearly it had been thought out for some time before. It detailed her grievances against her husband. He had yelled at her, called her "white trash," referred to her as "lazy-ass," told her she was stupid, showed no respect for her, insulted her friends, accused her of infidelities and pinched her girl friend's teats. She wrote that he was so wrapped up in himself that he ignored her needs, that he wouldn't get the house exterminated although he complained of the bugs, and finally, that he spent the money they had saved for a new house for him to go to school.

As we read the letter, Mr. Simpson interrupted to assure us that some of the charges weren't true, but still there was little anger. He cried, saying, "Now I can't stand the thought of not getting a chance to do things right." Then he blamed the friend for the separation. We focused again on the marital relationship. He expressed anger at the bugs, the friend, the cars, the school, and his tools. He said the neighbor had recommended the school and advised against exterminating the bugs. Several more efforts were made to focus on the wife. Finally we pointed out to him: "You're misdirecting your anger. There's always a man to pick up the pieces. You're blaming him for the problems between you and her. She must feel you're unable to change after six years of telling you what to do and your not doing it." After blaming a few more people, including a man at work who made him nervous and the hospital at which his baby was born, he agreed that "It looks like I always blame someone else, don't I. My troubles with my wife are mine. If I can't get my family back I'd like to find what's wrong. I'd ask too much without thinking. I see my brother-in-law, what he does for my sister, and how he enjoys it. My parents never showed any affection. My wife's taught my boy to love."

Finally he realized that, in this marriage as in his first, he could never admit he was wrong and never knew how to love someone else. He felt betrayed by his friend who "could have helped me and he didn't," but saw that the problems predated the friend and actually were part of a life long pattern of not knowing how to love. He saw that his first wife's infidelities further increased his distrust of close relationships. As he left, he was little less depressed, but we felt much progress had been made in putting the problems on a workable level.

Finally, on the third day, Mrs. Simpson and the two lawyers arrived. It was agreed that Mr. F. and Dr. P. would see the couple while the two lawyers and Miss D. observed from behind a one-way mirror.

First we spoke briefly with the two lawyers. Some excerpts from this conversation will clarify the atmosphere in which the interview was conducted.

HUSBAND'S LAWYER TO DR. P.—If she is not amenable to a reconciliation, I want him convinced of this and to accept it and let's get it over with.

HUSBAND'S LAWYER TO WIFE'S LAWYER—I don't want to get into any fights over custody whatsoever.

WIFE'S LAWYER TO DR. P.—OK, but here's another thing. You say you're working for Mr. Simpson's best interests. I think it's rather cruel to subject Mrs. Simpson to something like this.

DR. P.—I think you'll be surprised—What we're trying to do is to free ourselves of any sort of legal involvement so we can work with him and them. We always work with the family.

WIFE'S LAWYER—If it gets out of hand I'll step in and call it off. Is that fair enough?

DR. P.—Please do.

WIFE'S LAWYER—Well now, you see—if something, if uh, his lawyer, heard something and I came to the office next week and found a counter claim based on adultery, I would be extremely upset, not just with his lawyer, but with you.

DR. P.—Look, I have no—I don't know why you'd be mad with me because this woman has committed adultry—This is not my fault. I'm trying to help him. If the facts come out, I don't see how anybody can be—

WIFE'S LAWYER—Dr., I can understand your point.

DR. P.—If she's committed adultery, he has a right to know this. It doesn't sound as if she has and if she says she's not, well that's, you know, that should be good enough for him, but so far she hasn't even told him this much.

WIFE'S LAWYER—I think she could tell him to his face without a further confrontation.

DR. P.—I'm not working with his lawyer or with or for you.

WIFE'S LAWYER—Dr., I understand that—the only thing is—I'm not concerned about the medical problems here, I'm concerned about the legal problems. You're concerned about the medical.

(*Both lawyers agreed they were for a reconciliation.*)

HIS LAWYER—I do not plan, can't envision anything coming out I could use. I'm not paid for time. If something comes out we don't know about, will you withdraw from the case if I will?

DR. P.—The confusion between the two of you is as much as I see in most bad marriages. You're both very suspicious of one another.

WIFE'S LAWYER—No we're not.

HIS LAWYER—We're quite good friends. We have to protect our clients.

DR. P.—I know what it's like when I'm the psychiatrist for a woman and someone else is for her husband. We have to all four get together and work these things out.

WIFE'S LAWYER—I think it would be wise for us to sit in—

DR. P.—Look, we want Mrs. Simpson to fill out the same tests her husband did—these are for our records.

WIFE'S LAWYER—Now you're examining her.

(*Mrs. Simpson's lawyer was reassured.*)

WIFE'S LAWYER—I've dealt with many psychiatrists—I've never been asked to have a client go through something like this. If it's a criminal case, alright; but there's something different about this.

(*Dr. P. explains the workings of the Family Treatment Unit.*)

WIFE'S LAWYER—Doctor, our aims are a little antagonistic. She wants those children.

DR. P.—That's for the courts to decide. If either side tried to call me into the divorce proceedings, I'd do what I can to help the other side.

HIS LAWYER—This is an inexact science.

WIFE'S LAWYER—I'll talk to her. We're pioneering. Ground rules should be laid for this sort of thing.

HIS LAWYER—I think some good will come of this.

WIFE'S LAWYER—I hope so.

At this point, the two lawyers left the room, conferred with their clients, and joined Miss D. in the observing room behind the screen.

We hoped to accomplish several things in this interview. Foremost in the lawyers' minds was to settle any doubt about Mrs. Simpson's desire for a divorce, giving Mr. Simpson a chance to talk her out of it if he could. We had promised not to put any pressure on her to change her mind, but inherent in the situation was the implication that Mrs. Simpson should consider alternatives to divorce and should accept some guilt for hurting her husband by leaving him. We, of course, working with families, consider a divorce a poor way to end a family fight and something to be tried only after less drastic efforts fail. We hoped that a less drastic solution could be found. Our experience had been that few of the families which separate abruptly and one-sidedly remain separated long. Most of the families which were separated when we first saw them are now back together. Although in a few cases divorce may have been less destructive than continuing the chaotic marriages, the midst of a crisis or fight seems an inappropriate time to make such a drastic step.

Separations may be helpful, but calling in lawyers and judges with their emphasis on guilt and blame does not create an atmosphere conducive to problem-solving. Marital conflicts can't be worked out if one person must be the guilty party and the other the innocent. So, a second goal of the interview was to soften the legal battles. The legal mind, trained and chosen for its ability to see everything as all right or all wrong, could not be expected to react other than with confusion and distrust to our efforts to work with the nuances of marital interaction. But confusion would be preferable to vigorous dedication to conflicting truths, so we hoped to confuse the lawyers about their clients' rightness and their clients' spouses' wrongness. Hopefully, the two lawyers would work together to help the couple live, together or apart, with a minimum of chaos. At least, channels of communication could be opened.

The third goal was perhaps the most important. Doubting that a reconciliation was possible or that the lawyers would be less destructive in their efforts to help the couple destroy one another, we hoped to shift the arena of battle within Mr. Simpson from his relationship with the neighbor to the relationship with the wife. This could be done in part by just having Mrs. Simpson tell him she was leaving him and why. Through a confrontation we could dispel Mr. Simpson's fantasy that his wife was the helpless victim of the neighbor's evil influence, an idea encouraged by the neighbor and the lawyer.

With these primary goals in mind, Mr. F. and Dr. P. introduced themselves to Mrs. Simpson and ushered the couple into the interviewing room. Mrs. Simpson was a small woman, looking quite young. Fairly pretty and well built, she failed to be attractive because her clothes were fussy and wrinkled, her grooming haphazard, and her movements graceless and uncomfortable. She looked angry and determined and showed little desire to charm any of us. The room was set up with four chairs around a low circular coffee table. Mr. Simpson sat opposite his wife with Dr. P. and Mr. F. between them on either side. A large mirror along the wall shielded the observation room from view. A microphone hung unhidden from the ceiling.

The interview is not presented verbatim. The therapists' comments are presented almost intact, but the couples' statements are considerably condensed. Much repetition, particularly in Mr. Simpson's remarks, has been deleted. Major deletions are indicated. The intact interview lasted one and one-half hours. The session began as Dr. P. pointed out the one-way screen and microphone.

DR. P.—The tape recorder is on and your lawyers are behind the screen here with Miss D.Y. The purpose of all this is to make sure that nothing that goes on here between us will have any bearing on your divorce proceedings. I'm not going to testify at all.

Now, there are a lot of things you two need to say and to know. Can you explain to your wife why you wanted to see her?

MR. S.—(*Reciting, as a prepared speech*) Betty, I truly love you. I compare you to my mother. No matter what I did, I'd never lose your love—(*pauses*)

DR. P.—Why did it take him so long to realize he was being a lousy husband? What did you tell him?

MRS. S.—He'd holler at me and not help with the children, etc.

(*Mrs. S. angrily delivers her list of grievances, much as in the letter. We waited until she was through but did not encourage her to continue. Both spouses had prepared speeches and we felt it was necessary to them to speak their piece before we could proceed. Mrs. S. finished her speech, but Mr. S. ignored what she'd said and continued his speech.*)

MR. S.—You looked very beautiful New Years Eve. I know I'm a lousy dancer—

DR. P.—(*Interrupting*) Do you understand why she's leaving you? You're blaming every aspect of your life, but do you know?

MR. S.—(*Ignoring the interruption*) My neighbor put up the money for New Years Eve. It felt like heaven on earth with my wife in my arms, but now I pick up my tools and blame them because I'll never hold her again—(*pauses*)

DR. P.—Why are you leaving him? He still doesn't know.

MRS. S—(*Apologetically*) I don't love him anymore. I really don't know why. He called me a slut and made me feel terrible—

MR. S.—(Interrupting) I've accused her of other men, but I know now I was wrong. You cared about me at one time, you worried about me, you were glad to see me. If you'd come back, I'd go to church with you—

DR. P.—Is church the trouble?

MRS. S.—No.

DR. P.—What is the trouble?

MRS. S.—I've lost my love for him. Is there something wrong with me for that?

DR. P.—I don't know. I don't know what you're saying.

MR. F.—When did it change?

MRS. S.—About three years ago. He started blaming me, accusing me of going out with other men. He never had any trust for me.

MR. S.—I've never run around. I did take the money for the school.

DR. P.—Is it the money, or the school?

MRS. S.—No. (*this "no" sounded unsure.*)

DR. P.—How'd you feel about him investing money in the school rather than the house?

MRS. S.—I felt bad about it. He was working good—raising two children in a trailer isn't the thing. I did feel bad about it but I didn't tell him. If he'd made his mind up, he'd do it—

DR. P.—How did you feel about it?

MRS. S.—Hurt.

MR. S.—When I go to school each day I tell myself "if you hadn't done this, you'd still have your wife and kids"—I can't work on cars anymore—(*near tears*)

MR. F.—Did you feel he didn't spend enough time with you?

MRS. S.—No, not enough time with the kids.

MR. F.—Did you tell him?

MRS. S.—No.

DR. P.—Why didn't you tell him?

MRS. S.—He bought cars I told him not to—

MR. S.—I never understood my buying junk cars—

DR. P.—(*Sympathetically, but firmly*) That's no excuse Mr. Simpson. You're still responsible for what you do.

MR. S.—I never looked at what a car was, but what it could be.

DR. P.—It's a shame you never looked at your marriage that way.

Here Dr. P. began to be critical of Mr. Simpson as a husband hoping to encourage Mrs. Simpson to attack him, which she couldn't do so long as he remained pleading and pathetic. Accomplishing our three goals would require that Mrs. Simpson directly attack her husband so that he could know he'd been attacked, so that her feelings could be revealed, and so that the lawyers could be faced with the reality of the marital interaction. This was, in effect, giving Mrs. Simpson permission to ignore his pathetic depression and attack him for the things he'd done before. Mr. F. likewise focused on the past and the therapists both were critical of Mrs. Simpson for withholding her grievances. Throughout they both had to avoid the appearance of pushing this angry, defiant woman into going back to her husband.

MR. S.—I truly love my wife. I can't understand how I could be so foolish. Me and the neighbor—

DR. P.—What's the situation? The neighbor?

MR. S.—I've been under his influence for four years.

MRS. S.—He took him for his father.

DR. P.—Did you tell him how you felt about that?

MRS. S.—(*Defensively*) No. I never felt I had a right to tell him anything. I had no education. I came from a broken marriage. My father was always in the hospital. It was a broken home with everyone unhappy. I could never say anything.

DR. P.—Your husband's been blaming the neighbor.

MRS S.—(*Angry*) A man old enough to be my father! Well Wilbur, there's nothing between us!

MR. S.—He's lied to me and to you. The things he's told me aren't things that would help a man keep his sanity. He said he'd help you get away from me.

MRS. S.—He brings over milk. That's all.

DR. P.—How does it make you feel to be accused of an affair with him?

MRS. S.—Cheap! (*Angry and glaring at her husband*)

MR. S.—(*Returning to speech*) I never knew the meaning of the word love until I met you.

DR. P.—Mr. Simpson, you didn't know the meaning until she left you. You showed no evidence of it during the marriage. You know the meaning of depression, loss, futility, emptiness, but I wonder about love, whether you know what you're talking about.

MR. S.—I wanted her every night, but I haven't had any sexual urges since she left. She tried to get me to bathe and now I bathe every day.

MRS. S.—Wilbur, that's not the thing! The reason I left is—is that I don't love you anymore; because you never showed any trust for me, and love for me!

MR. S.—I never showed it Betty, but it's there, honey, it is—

MRS. S.—Why couldn't you have shown this six years ago?

MR. S.—It's there—the love is there. I can't stand to think of another woman. I see families, husbands carrying children—they're having a wonderful time. I'd like to sell the trailer, rent a house, etc.—(*He continues to plead.*)

MRS. S.—Will you please understand this. If there's no more love on my side, how can the kids be happy when I couldn't be?

MR. S.—Please, etc.—(*crying and begging her to come back.*)

MRS. S.—Why did you get a lawyer? Because you want to take the children away from me? Because you want to hurt me?

MR. F.—Do you want to hurt her?

MR. S.—No.

MR. F.—Then why file a counterclaim?

MRS. S.—I told you you could see the kids.

MR. S.—I didn't understand the restraining order.

MRS. S.—I've seen you blow up before when you've been hurt.

DR. P.—When was this?

MRS. S.—The first time I left him.

DR. P.—What happened then?

MRS. S.—I went back.

MR. S.—I was very very happy when you came back.

MRS. S.—Within a month you were back insulting me again, in your own way, calling me a slut. You never had any trust for me, never—

MR. S.—(*Pitifully*) Right now I feel it's all hopeless and lost but I feel I can trust you with anything.

MRS. S.—(*Angry*) You'd read the mileage on the car to see if I'd been out.

MR. F.—How'd the two of you meet?

Here Mr. F. felt the attack had been sufficient. Apparently, he also felt the marriage should be evaluated for the possibility of a reconciliation, something which could be done now that the atmosphere was one of honest expression of angry feelings.

MR. S.—My wife was wild before we met.

MRS. S.—I was seventeen.

MR. S.—I'd heard the guys at the service station talking about her. I was looking for a girl to go to bed with. I never believed what they said.

DR. P.—Were the things true?

MRS. S.—(*Matter of factly*) Yeah.

MR. S.—We have an old trunk, I'd like for us to open it together. I know there'd be happy moments for us, if we could only live together. I want a chance. How would you feel if the kids were taken away from you and you could only see them three hours a week and all they could talk about was Uncle Bob (the neighbor) because they see him twelve to fourteen hours a day.

MRS. S.—(*Suspiciously, suddenly alarmed*) What did they say?

MR. S.—I won't tell you. You might take it out on them.

MRS. S.—There goes your trust again.

DR. P.—You have very little trust for her.

MRS. S.—In your own mind you can't trust me, so why do you want me back?

MR. S.—I want a chance to try.

DR. P.—Just how happy were the two of you when you were together?

MR. S.—Not the last month. Up until then we were happy. I see my sister and brother-in-law, etc.

DR. P.—You're still thinking in terms of romantic notions rather than cold hard facts of what it was like. It wasn't all that great. You were busy running out checking the speedometer, you were tied up with your cars, and didn't care what she was doing.

MR. S.—That was true in the past; now I can see how wonderful things could have been. If I were just given another chance.

MR. F.—What did you do when you were angry with him?

MRS. S.—I'd blow my top.

DR. P.—And it had no effect. You gave him another chance five years ago.

MRS. S.—He acted like he didn't love me. My parents' marriage was bad, but they loved us and taught us love. But he treated me like a two year old.

DR. P.—What was the last straw?

MRS. S.—I couldn't take it anymore. Would you call me crazy to leave?

DR. P.—You've asked that twice. I don't even think *he's* crazy.

MR. S.—(*Begs for another chance again.*)

DR. P.—How often does he get like this—begs and talks about how terrible he is?

MRS. S.—When I left before. I guess you'd say I loved him then. I quit three years ago. These little things just built up.

DR. P.—Did you ever try to get help?

MRS. S.—No—I figured it would cost too much money.

MR. S.—If we'd known this would be available, we'd have tried. I remember Bobby learning to walk and now the baby is crawling and I'll never see her learn to walk.

MR. F.—How many children?

MRS. S.—Two.

MR. F.—Ages?

MRS. S.—Four and ten months.

MR. F.—Did he show much interest in them?

MRS. S.—I can't remember him showing any interest.

MR. S.—I could have had a wonderful time with my children. I never realized it before . . . .

DR. P.—Mr. Simpson, this marriage has meant damm little to you for six years and now you're trying to convince your wife she should believe you when you say you're capable of changing completely.

MR. S.—I am capable of changing completely.

DR. P.—I believe this, but how in the devil do you expect her to believe this after six years of making no effort whatever, even after she gave you an ultimatum?

MR. S.—I just pray to the good Lord. It's asking a whole lot.

DR. P.—What would he have to do?

MR. S.—Betty, please.

MRS. S.—Wilbur, you're a grown man—quit begging.

MR. S.—I've got to try (*begs more*) I know now that it doesn't take money.

MRS. S.—Why couldn't you realize this before?

DR. P.—You're blaming the cars and the school. It's you. You were taking everything for granted. You didn't trust her. You think she might have left because she was under the influence of someone else, but you can't blame her, she's easily influenced.

MR. S.—The fault is mine.

DR. P.—It was between you. If there were another man, it would be someone who caught her when she ran out of the house—but she certainly had every reason to go screaming out of the house into the arms of whoever was coming along.

MR. S.—She's never lied to me.

DR. P.—You've had doubts about her and the neighbor.

MR. S.—I felt I could trust her, but not him.

DR. P.—What's he getting out of it? Why is he helping you?

We wanted to understand the neighbor's role better. As it developed, a major accomplishment of the interview was helping Mrs. Simpson see that the neighbor was lying to both of them. It was the start of an alliance between Mr. and Mrs. Simpson.

MR. S.—I don't know—he's not getting a thing out of me.

DR. P.—Do you understand why he suspects you?

MR. S.—Remember, he used to telephone all these girls. He dropped that when you left.

MRS. S.—Wilbur, there were times I wanted to go out and you didn't and he did, so we went out and you knew about it but nothing's happening now.

DR. P.—Mrs. Simpson, he suspects you and the neighbor because he didn't understand these things and he felt betrayed by him. It seems reasonable for him to suspect this until you tell him the truth and clear it up.

MRS. S.—Wilbur, there's nothing between us.

MR. S.—He talked me out of going to church—now that I'm away from his influence, I can be different.

MRS. S.—You've always found a father image.

MR. F.—Did you feel he didn't confide in you enough?

MRS. S.—Yes. It took him three months to tell me about his first marriage.

MR. S.—I was sick about it.

DR. P.—(*Impatiently*) Mr. Simpson—you're continuing to tell us how pitiful you are. We've heard this. Your wife's heard it too. How'd you feel about his turning to other men rather than you?

MRS. S.—Hurt—he treated me like I didn't have enough brains.

DR. P.—Were you concerned about this?

MRS. S.—Yeah. I didn't have much education. It's been eating on me since the eighth grade. My spelling is bad. The way he'd help me would make me feel like a child.

DR. P.—You were a child when he married you. It was OK at first, but you haven't let him know what you expected of him. Perhaps it's hard to get a message to him.

MRS. S.—Yes.

DR. P.—Do you have much faith in his ability to change? If he changed in a few years, would it matter to you? Has he hurt you this much?

MRS. S.—No, I don't love him.

DR. P.—You feel what he felt when you married him. This first wife had been unfaithful, he expected you to be. If you get this divorce and you leave him alone, how will this leave him so far as seeing the kids?

MRS. S.—He can see them whenever he wants.

DR. P.—Mr. Simpson, if you work things out more pleasantly with your wife, you'll have the kids more than you had them when you were married.

MR. S.—I can't believe she won't give me another chance. I'll never be happy if we don't have another chance.

DR. P.—Your wife says change first, come asking later.

MRS. S.—Wilbur, I've seen you do this before. I couldn't go back to you now—I don't think I ever could.

MR. S.—You're not leaving me much hope. My throat is dry, can I get some water? (*Steps out for water*)

DR. P.—How does he make you feel?

MRS. S.—Pity for him.

(*Mr. Simpson returns*)

DR. P.—Tell him.

MRS. S.—I just feel pity for you. It won't work on these conditions.

MR. S.—Why is the good Lord refusing me a chance?

DR. P.—The good Lord isn't refusing you anything. You've flubbed the dub for about six years and it's catching up with you. Now, your wife says that she doesn't want to go back to you. She's saying that pretty clearly. She's going to be available, around—there's no other man—

MR. S.—If I invited you for dinner, would you go out with me?

MRS. S.—I might. Look Wilbur—I ain't gonna go back to you.

MR. S.—Never? I can't face it.

MRS. S.—I've lost my love for you.

MR. S.—Mine is there. I can't believe there'll be no chance again.

DR. P.—Your wife is saying "change."

MR. S.—I can't continue in school.

DR. P.—You can. This is something we can work on later. Would you like to see your kids more?

MR. S.—With my wife?

DR. P.—She doesn't want to see you.

MRS. S.—(*Angrily*) All I can feel for you is pity, *pity!*

DR. P.—And anger, which you're expressing right now. How do the kids feel about him?

MRS. S.—Bobby asks about him once in awhile, once in awhile.

MR. S.—Do you feel it's fair for my kids to spend 12-14 hours a day with him?

MRS. S.—They won't now. I chased him off.

MR. S.—That makes me feel considerably better.

MRS. S.—The only time he comes over is when he picks his car up, if you'd get me a car, then . . . .

MR. S.—Betty, I offered to give you a car, through Bob, and I asked him about it repeatedly and he said she doesn't want your car, she wants my car, I'm giving her my car, she wants my car, your car isn't good enough!

MRS. S.—(*Startled*) He was lying to you.

MR. S.—Well, that's what he told me.

MRS. S.—He's lying to you.

DR. P.—Do either of you think you can trust Bob as a way of handling both of your lives? Is Bob a good person to run either one of your lives?

MRS. S.—He's not running my life.

DR. P.—Is he a good person to get involved in your lives?

MR. S.—Actually, he's a very immoral man, but I never realized the situation before this.

DR. P.—As you see, he's lying to you too. Whether you're involved with him or not, I'd be suspicious about what he had in mind long term. That's up to you to decide. He's not doing a very good job of running your lives. At one point sometime ago, he could have been of help to you in working out some of these things. Apparently both of you told him your problems and all he did was sabotage it. I'd be careful about him.

MR. S.—He told me you used to talk to him for hours on the phone about your troubles.

MRS. S.—(*Again startled*) On the phone!

Mrs. Simpson was shaken by these revelations of the neighbor's treachery. As she reacted to this, Mr. Simpson became more assertive and almost adequate. For the first time, he did not act depressed and pitiful. Mrs. Simpson briefly seemed a little dependent on her husband. She almost seemed apologetic for having left him. We felt this was a good time to end the interview, leaving the relationships at this point, quite improved from the preinterview level.

MR. S.—He said you told him things most women wouldn't tell other women, and a lot of things he told me were things nobody would have told him but you. If he'd told me at the time, we could have seen people like this. Instead he kept this inside him, looking for a way to turn it to his advantage. I knew he'd be trying.

MRS. S.—He'd never do any good. He never tried.

MR. F.—Why did you run him away?

MRS. S.—I didn't want him around no more. Bobby goes over there and talks about him. I don't want that.

MR. S.—Bobby was getting sleepy and wanted his blanket. I asked him if he slept with Mommy. He said Uncle Bob sleeps with Mommy too. I said does Marvin, he said no.

MRS. S.—It's not true—and you believed him?

MR. S.—No—I could give you the time he goes, the times he leaves, the places you go. That's what I'd do to get the children away. (*Begs again*).

MRS. S.—It couldn't work.

DR. P.—A divorce is just a piece of paper. The feelings are the same, with or without the paper. A certain percentage of people get back together.

MR. S.—The kids were always available before. Now I have to go to my lawyer and he goes to your lawyer and he goes to you before I can see them.

DR. P.—Can you work these things out?

MRS. S.—Yeah, but why didn't you care about the kids before—

DR. P.—Your wife will get a divorce. Getting the kids would be impractical for you. You'd give them to your parents like you did before.

MR. S.—Betty, this is the first chance I've had to talk with you, right? All I've had to go on was what Bob would tell me and my lawyer—true? And you and I both know Bob is as two-faced as they come and he's probably the world's most perfect liar.

MRS. S.—Why do you keep bringing him up?

MR. S.—He's the only contact I've had since the restraining order. (*pauses*) I'd like to ask you about the trailer, do you want to move in next to Bob or shall I move it?

DR. P.—Would you feel better if you moved it?

MR. S.—I don't want him around my kids.

MRS. S.—I don't want to keep the kids away from you. If I were really angry, I'd kept them away.

MR. S.—You won't turn them against me?

MRS. S.—I never have.

DR. P.—OK. Mrs. Simpson, can you fill out some forms (*explains*). We'll be happy to see you anytime you'd like about anything You'll be involved with one another, divorce or no. If you need to fight and need a referee, call us.

MR. S.—Will you, if I change—

DR. P.—You're trying to pin her down. You didn't change. You didn't let him know what you wanted. At present you can't live together, but don't avoid one another and accuse one another. You've still got a world and two children to share. Don't go through Bob. Go through your lawyers until they let you go directly.

(*Therapists step out*)

MR. S.—(*Discuss trailer*) Did Bob bring a loaded gun to you? He told me that he brought it to you and told me your address so I'd go there and you'd shoot me.

MRS. S.—That's true.

MR. S.—I'll move the trailer away from him.

MRS. S.—Fine.

As we left, the couple was doing some cooperative problem solving for the first time since she had left him. The interview had accomplished one thing we didn't think possible, i.e., establishing an alliance between husband and wife against the neighbor who had betrayed them both. We had also learned that Mr. Simpson's picture of the neighbor's role was not extremely exaggerated. An immediate reconciliation did not seem likely, but an eventual one remained possible. Mr. Simpson could not ignore his wife's anger or the reasons for it and had clear direction for change in himself. Most interestingly, the two lawyers had been shaken by the interview. Mr. Simpson's lawyer had to realize that the neighbor was not the only source of friction and he was disenchanted with his client as a martyr. Mrs. Simpson's lawyer had been sympathetic with Mr. Simpson's plight and wanted a reconciliation. Not completely in jest, they spoke of switching clients. They agreed to cooperate with one another in helping the Simpsons solve their problems.

In this one interview enough had happened to change dramatically the crisis situation. These things could not have been accomplished without the conjoint participation of at least four of the five principals. Attempting to involve the neighbor would have been interesting and valuable, but impractical, even if he had been willing to come in, because our effort was to improve communication between the husband and wife by disentangling him from their lives and from Mr. Simpson's fantasies. A meeting with the couple and the neighbor would be contraindicated as an initial meeting, and would be problematic even after several joint sessions with the couple.

While we often call friends or ex-spouses for information or understanding of a crisis, we have found that involving them in treatment is useful when the relationship is going to continue to be a close and important one, as with the no-longer married parents of young children. Ex-spouses and friends are usually quite willing to be seen and often strikingly helpful.

What would have happened if the Simpson's neighbor had been seen? We don't know. We might have considered it if we had not received a call from Mr. Simpson the morning after the conjoint interview. He was feeling much better, was making arrangements to give his wife a car and medical insurance, had arranged to have the children for the weekend, and had returned to school, no longer blaming it for the separation. One encouraging remark, indicating that he was beginning to accept the loss was, "I don't think I'll ever be able to marry again after my wife remarries."

Two days later he was seen in the office. Over the weekend, as he begged his wife to return to him, she got mad and threatened to limit his visiting time with the children if he kept playing on her sympathy. We discussed his future, insisting that he take his medicine, continue in school, and go to work, and pointed out that his only hope for reconciliation was in changing himself by learning to understand women as people. Accordingly, we suggested that he enter a long-term outpatient mixed psychotherapy group.

It is typical for us to begin termination early in treatment to lessen the effects of the dependency we create through our availability, directiveness, and supportiveness. We like to terminate in a state of positive transference as the families will return in subsequent crises, but we find that when we neglect to stress from the beginning that the therapeutic relationship will be of short duration, patients become overly dependent and have a recurrence of symptoms when we attempt to withdraw from their lives. So we begin long-term treatment planning as soon as possible. In this case, group therapy was available and seemed well suited to Mr. Simpson's needs.

Two days later Mr. Simpson called to tell us he felt good enough to move from his sister's home to a furnished room near his new janitorial job and the mechanics school. Mrs. Simpson had encouraged him to break the restraining order and the countersuit. Mrs. Simpson still planned to get the divorce, despite her lawyer's feeling that she should consider alternatives. We decided to see the couple together again, a move approved by both lawyers and the couple. It was set for the next day.

Mrs. Simpson called to cancel the joint interview. She felt confused and ambivalent and did not want to be pressured into a reconciliation since she doubted that it could work until her husband changed. Mr. Simpson was surprisingly accepting of his wife's feelings. He was thrilled at the prospect of entering a group to learn about people. He discussed his many hobbies and his interest in mechanical things. He described his confusion and suspiciousness of other people, particularly women, relating this to his enigmatic and unloving mother. We advised him to contact the group leader and reminded him that we were available at any time.

A month later, Mr. Simpson called requesting an appointment. He was seen that afternoon. His only concern was that the group had not begun. Dr. P. called the group leader and found the group would begin meeting in one more week. Mr. and Mrs. Simpson were having frequent contacts, though Mrs. Simpson did not want to stop the divorce since she frankly enjoyed promiscuity, had indulged these desires, and wanted to continue it for awhile longer. The aspect of their relationship the Simpsons were enjoying most was their planning of tricks to pull on the neighbor, who was still expected to pay for the divorce. Mrs. Simpson had avoided the neighbor's continuing efforts to seduce her, while she flaunted her other affairs before him. Mr. Simpson was working, going to school, and feeling good without medication.

For six months, our only contact with the Simpsons was through the group leaders, who reported that he was attending weekly but having difficulty understanding or discussing feelings.

Six months after our initial contacts with the family, a follow-up was done by a social worker. The divorce was now final. Mr. Simpson was still living in the boarding house. He had gotten a better job and was still in school, doing well at both. He remained preoccupied with his relationship with his ex-wife. He felt he was resigned to the divorce, especially since his contacts with his children were frequent and enjoyable, but his wife continued to alternately seduce him and reject him. He felt lonely and isolated, but still enjoyed contacts with his sister and brother-in-law, as well as long talks with his landlady. He did not feel comfortable in the group, though it was helping him. He was not depressed.

Four months later, he was still in the group. He called, asked for an appointment, and was seen later in the day to discuss the possibility of our seeing his wife. They had reconciled, briefly, but she decided she liked her freedom to sleep with other men. She now wanted to give him the children. We told him that we would see Mrs. Simpson if she wanted us to. He agreed to try to talk his wife into seeing us. We suggested that in either case, he continue with the group. We were impressed with how well Mr. Simpson was doing and his equanimity about which decision his wife would make. Mrs. Simpson did not choose to come in and Mr. Simpson did not press the matter.

Two months later, Mr. and Mrs. Simpson moved to another state where he, after he finished the school, had found a job as an auto mechanic.

Another year later, two years after our initial contacts with the family, a partial long distance follow-up was done. The Simpsons were still together, though they had not officially remarried. There were conflicts over her job as a bar waitress in a nightclub, but she seemed fairly sure that she would stay with her husband. The relationship, though hardly ideal, satisfied them both. Mr. Simpson was doing quite well financially since he had opened a highly specialized laundry business. Mrs. Simpson was proud of this success. There had been no recurrence of his depression or paranoia and no new symptoms.

In reconsidering this case after a two year follow-up, we might wonder what more could have been done to improve the marital relationship. In our limited contacts, we tried to resolve a crisis and did this fairly successfully, but we did little to change the long-term interactional patterns of the couple. This is in accordance with the goals we ordinarily set. We rely on referrals for real change. Mr. Simpson made minimal use of the long-term group therapy, but must have changed enough to convince his wife to come back to him and stay with him. She, unfortunately, did not change. Apparently she emulates her mother and is comfortable only when she has freedom from marriage and the expectation of fidelity, a situation Mr. Simpson tolerates amazingly well. His financial success may even be influenced by her demands and threats. The relationship, while hardly ideal, is permitting Mr. Simpson's successful functioning and is acceptable to both. In comparison with the marriages they have known, particularly his first marriage and those of their parents and siblings, it is a good relationship, which may even improve with time.

This case is one in which marital separation was the crisis leading to the development of symptoms and the request for hospitalization. As in this case, the stress which produces the separation is rarely just chronic dissatisfaction with the relationship. Often there is the entry of some new features into the conflict or the removal of some balancing force which previously made the marriage bearable. A common pattern, as seen in the Simpson family, develops when one spouse, angry over a repetition of a chronic conflict, seeks and finds someone else who encourages separation as the solution.

Intrafamilial stresses also can lead to separation. The birth of a child for instance, may bring an increase in ungratified emotional demands from both partners. Several separations in our series followed retirement or the "empty nest syndrome," in which the children grow up and leave home. In each case, the parents face an unbuffering of their sterile or hostile relationship. Other intra-familial stresses which occasionally lead to separation are vaca-tions, periods of unemployment, or illnesses. In these situations also, the couple is forced into a closer relationship than usual and the chronic conflicts take on heightened significance.

At the initial interview, the couple may ignore these new factors as they focus only on the old problems that the family has lived with all these years. To accept their assessment of the problem's chronicity would be to miss the point of the crisis and to assume the marriage has always been as bad as it seems at the time.

Treating a marital crisis involves the same nonspecific sympto-matic relief described in the previous chapters. There are several specific steps. First, communication is reopened. This may be automatic or may, as with the Simpsons, require considerable effort. Sometimes the separated spouse will not come in, but rarely is it impossible to establish telephone contact long enough to clarify his grievances and intentions. Many times, "flame fanners"—those relatives or professional "helpers," in the Simpson case the lawyers and the neighbor, who find a crisis and heighten it by keeping the battle going and the communication muddled—have to be removed from the scene, as was the neighbor, or enlisted, as were the law-yers, in support of the marriage rather than on the side of one of the combatants.

Once communication is reopened, the crisis can be defined and placed in perspective. This involves deemphasizing the present dis-satisfaction long enough to find out when the marriage became in-tolerable rather than just imperfect, why this change occurred, and whether the family can return to the usual state of tolerable dissatisfaction. If changes are demanded, these can be negotiated while a separation or divorce is postponed. Usually the necessary changes are possible—even minimal.

Tasks, demonstrating each partner's willingness to make these changes, are suggested, negotiated, and assigned, and the good faith of each partner thereby tested. Tasks for couples on the brink of divorce have included mutual activities such as sex, making new schedules or budgets, discussing some problem, planning together for some common goal, and just going out together. Individual tasks, besides breaking off certain extrafamilial contacts, have included job seeking, job changing, cleaning the house, stopping drinking, and improved functioning in conflictual areas. In all cases, the task conforms with the couple's view of what is appropriate. The task usually represents a return to a previous level and pattern of functioning. The focus of therapy can shift from chronic grievances and failures to the performance of the assigned tasks. The same conflicts will appear in the performance of the tasks and can be dealt with as current reality rather than past history and thus relatively free of recriminations and distortions.

As negotiations continue, it may become apparent that one spouse will not live with the other unless he is different from the way he has always been, in which case he can choose between separation and change. If separation is chosen, this is made as conflict-free and nondestructive as possible, as seemed to be the case with the Simpsons. If change is chosen, referral for long-term therapy for the couple or one partner may be made. The decision to refer becomes a highly individual one.

Once the plan for change in the marriage is made and agreed upon, termination is made, sometimes with the expectation of subsequent crises. These subsequent crises can usually be handled in a single telephone call, but may require renegotiation of roles and rules, or a referral.

The goal of this therapeutic process, intrusive as it may seem in the initial phases and incomplete in the final ones, is to bring about a rapid return to the most familiar patterns of family functioning which still allow the couple to live together without driving one another crazy.

CHAPTER 5

Acute Psychosis in an Adolescent: A Crisis of Development

The Family Treatment Unit has worked with a number of families whose problems stem from the emancipatory strivings of adolescents and young adults from their parents. These kinds of problems may be seen in any family, regardless of who is the identified patient, as any member of the family may be the symptom bearer.

The family containing an adolescent is in a state of flux with difficult and basic changes which are potentially disruptive to individual and family nature. No longer can the parents view the children as completely dependent upon them but instead, this is a time in the family life cycle when the family must normally prepare and give impetus to the children to begin thinking of a life apart from the parents. The Family Treatment Unit has seen a variety of family situations in which the crises have to do with children leaving home to go to college, marry or join the service; or if remaining in the family, they are asking for more freedom and a change of their role within the family.

What follows is the presentation of a very chaotic and destructive family situation which offered negligible support to the identified patient Portia Jones, eighteen, in making these changes. Since her graduation from high school one year previously, Portia had been struggling to secure steady employment, frequently changing jobs, experiencing a variety of living situations, and finally returning home in a highly disturbed emotional state.

The Jones family illustrates the work of the Family Treatment Unit from two standpoints. First, it demonstrates how family oriented outpatient crisis treatment deals with an acutely psychotic patient through home visits, office visits, twenty-four hour availability and medication. Secondly, it points up the Family Treatment Unit's sense of continuing responsibility and involvement in the referral process once the crisis treatment is over, so as to be available to the referring agency on a consultant basis and to the family in case of any future crisis.

First Day:

According to the admitting note of the psychiatric resident, the patient was an "eighteen year old, white, single female, brought in by her mother. The patient graduated from high school last year and was living with a girlfriend until one month ago when her father took her back home because of unusual behavior—crying, laughing, and mother states she frequently laughs and says she is fearful as if someone is hurting her. Impression: acute schizophrenic reaction. Disposition: admission."

Mr. F., the team Psychiatric Social Worker, met with Portia and her mother in the emergency room. She was mute with a fixed, blank stare, clinging to her mother. Portia was dressed in a bathrobe and appeared disheveled. Mrs. Jones, thirty-eight, was very anxious and frightened of her daughter's condition but held herself back from crying with great restraint and showed herself to be distraught over her daughter's condition. Portia was of medium height and build, with a pale, freckled complexion. Throughout the emergency room contact she said little, but infrequently responded to questions with a nod of the head and several times whiningly expressed the feeling that she wanted someone to save her and care for her.

Mrs. Jones explained that for the past four weeks Portia had been in this condition, talking very little but staying around the house, anxiously clinging to her parents. She had slept little and cried constantly. The parents had tried to pull her out of this condition through pleading and prayer meetings. Feeling that Portia was not getting any better, Mrs. Jones spoke with a neighbor who suggested that the girl be brought to the emergency room. Mrs. Jones said that after Portia's graduation from high school a year ago, the girl secured a baby-sitting job and moved away from home to live with a friend. She held a number of baby-sitting jobs throughout the year and finally went to work with her paternal grandmother to care for a ninety-five year old senile woman. Portia and her grandmother quarreled frequently, mostly because of the restrictiveness of the grandmother over the girl's dating. About six weeks ago the grandmother noticed that she was very slow in her movements and would not do her job, so she was taken home by her father.

Rather guiltily, Mrs. Jones confessed that she had not been very close to her daughter as Portia was a girl with whom it was hard to be affectionate and loving. Mrs. Jones felt very bad when Portia did not come directly to her following a reported rape in December of the previous year. Instead, Portia told her grandmother about it three months later, and the grandmother told the parents. Mrs. Jones had always felt her daughter capable of handling people on the outside, but this incident and what had been happening lately had made her wonder how she had failed her daughter.

The contact in the emergency room provided some background information about Portia, but all attempts to have the girl verbally involve herself in the interview were to no avail. After talking with Mrs. Jones and Portia in the emergency room for about forty-five minutes, Mr. F. took them over to the Family Treatment Unit offices where he hoped that the team would be able to speak to the rest of the family. In the office Mrs. Jones called her husband who was a laborer for the Parks Department, and he agreed to come to the office immediately after work (about 4 p.m.), along with his other daughter Hilda, sixteen. The only son Jimmy, fourteen, was away at summer camp.

Mr. F. discussed the results of the emergency room contact with the team. At 4 p.m. that day, Dr. P. and Mr. F. interviewed the Jones family. Mr. Jones came to the office immediately after work, bringing Hilda. Mr. Jones was of stocky build, medium height, and prided himself on his physical prowess, offering to lift Dr. P. with a bear hug; and also proud that he was free from having any bad habits such as drinking and smoking. These comments were particularly in reference to Dr. P's. smoking. Mr. Jones appeared very warm and affectionate towards Portia, but in trying to express his concern about his daughter, dominated the interview by engaging in a paranoid tirade about how the world had mistreated him. He said that the world was tough and rough with very little consideration for people and that his only solace was religion, and showed everyone a worn pocket-sized Bible. For the past two years he had been very interested in church work and attended Baptist church services several times a week. He was proud that despite a fourth grade education he had taught himself to read the Bible.

Throughout the harangue, the rest of the Jones family sat idly by, seemingly oblivious, the only noticeable reaction being Hilda's constant squirming in her chair, giggling and making light of Portia's situation. Mr. Jones continued to ramble on and on, becoming more agitated and gradually had to be brought back to the point of the interview, which was to talk about his family and Portia. This was the first marriage for both Mr. Jones and his wife. There was no history of other members of the family receiving any psychiatric help. The Joneses admitted that at times they had argued pretty heatedly and there had been open talk of divorce, but that they passed this off and in the main they got along quite well. The parents were very reserved with each other as they mostly talked to the team. Mr. and Mrs. Jones were sincerely concerned about their daughter and were quite willing to go along with any plans offered by the team.

Mr. Jones described Portia as being retarded, very slow about doing things and making decisions. She was always delaying, and whenever they had any place to go, she was always the last one to be completely dressed. He compared her with his other daughter Hilda, who was more lively and alert, though she had not done as well as Portia had in school.

After we had talked with the family for about an hour, Portia was still quite withdrawn, mute, and clinging strongly to her parents, but beginning to respond to the team as repeated offers of help were made to her. She had picked up the family's attitude about the outside world being a very frightening, hostile place. Her failure to hold a job and her alleged sexual experiences had reinforced the parents' attitude that the outside world was no good, that she was incompetent to cope with it. Dr. P. immediately placed her on medication, but she resisted taking a chlorpromazine spansule. After much persuasion and the threat of injection, she finally agreed. Hilda particularly became rather impatient with Portia and could not tolerate her sister's resistance to the medication as she was hungry and wanted to get home as soon as possible. The immediate treatment goal with the Joneses was to help Portia reconstitute herself to the point where she was less withdrawn. The family was seen as allies in helping her get over the acute period. How extensive our goals could be with this family in trying to change their expectations and image of Portia seemed quite open to question at this point. It was interesting that at the end of the interview Portia was a bit more nonverbally responsive, particularly to her father, and clung to him. The family agreed to the Family Treatment Unit's coming out to make a home visit the following morning. We intended to see only Portia and Mrs. Jones during the home visit. Dr. P. told the family that Portia was quite upset, and with the medication she would get some needed rest. They were not to expect too much of her at this point except sleep. To go further was inadvisable.

The Next Morning:

Miss D. and Mr. F. went out to the Jones home, a two bedroom frame house with an attractive lawn and exterior. However, the interior looked rather bleak and depressing and was drably furnished. Mrs. Jones looked haggard and said that Portia had been very agitated and had finally slept at 1:30 a.m. During the early part of the evening, she had been in bed with her parents pleading with them to take care of her. Mrs. Jones felt that this had gotten completely out of hand, as Portia had tried to get sexually intimate with both parents. This upset Mrs. Jones very much and for awhile she thought she would have to restrain her husband, who might lose sight of his role as father and engage in sexual activity with their daughter. She said that the night before Portia had tried the same thing with her sister Hilda. For this reason, the mother felt that she did not want to bring her son, Jimmy, home from camp that weekend and wanted to wait until Portia got better. It was obvious that this was more in the nature of regressive infantile demanding behavior than of sexual activity on Portia's part. We reassured Mrs. Jones that she had capably handled the situation.

There was more discussion about Portia's behavior during the past year. Mrs. Jones was still very much hurt about the fact that she had only recently found out that her daughter had been raped last Christmas. The circumstances of the rape as described by Portia, were such that she had led the man on and could have avoided the situation. She was sharply criticized and not allowed to go out on any more dates. Portia told the grandmother that she had had sexual experiences with many other boys but had denied this to her mother and said that she had exaggerated in order to upset the grandmother, who was described as a religious fanatic who felt that Portia was evil. Mrs. Jones now thought in retrospect that she had done the wrong thing in being so critical of her daughter. She said that Portia had done well in school up until the tenth grade when her grades fell off and she started going out with boys. The mother said that she had informed Portia about menstruation and other factors related to sex at puberty.

As in the first interview, Mrs. Jones made it clear that she knows very well how to handle her husband. She said that she does not agree with him about his excessive religious devotion but did go along with him. She had often physically wrestled with her husband when there had been serious arguments and knew how to handle his temper outbursts.

In showing us about the house, Mrs. Jones said that the boy slept downstairs and since Portia's behavior of late, Hilda was also occupying a basement bedroom. The mother looked very tired and worn out from staying up so late with Portia and talked about wanting to take her daughter to the hospital again in an ambulance. When Portia woke up later on in the interview, the girl did a lot of crying and was uncontrollable. It appeared as if the medication needed to be evaluated and it was arranged that Dr. P. and Miss D. would go out later in the afternoon to further assess the situation.

Following this contact it was apparent that unless Portia's behavior was stabilized, the mother would not continue to care for her at home. Mrs. Jones had been dealing with the girl's schizophrenic behavior for several weeks and was on the verge herself of being completely worn out. The description of Portia's behavior the night before vividly pointed out the pressures and demands under which a family is placed in coping with an acutely psychotic member. The response of Mr. Jones was fascinating and revealed his incestuous wishes which were staved off by Mrs. Jones' separating the father and daughter. One might question the advisability of leaving Portia in this kind of a situation and not hospitalizing her, however, we decided to see if it was clinically possible to treat someone this disturbed at home. In the Jones case, we thought the mother was a resourceful person, who with our support, could be helped to tolerate a great deal of Portia's behavior until the girl got over her acute psychotic symptoms. Consequently, a second home visit was planned by the Family Treatment Unit for that afternoon to lend weight and authority to our plan, and Dr. P. and Miss D. made the visit at 3:00 p.m.

Mrs. Jones had apparently taken a nap and looked more rested than she had in the morning. She had managed to give Portia some oral chlorpromazine and the daughter had slept for the past three hours, so it was decided that a shot was not necessary. Dr. P. advised Mrs. Jones that the sexual behavior her daughter was exhibiting was not really sexual but infantile, and this reassured the mother immensely. The team left shortly after this having advised the family that they could get in touch with us if there were any further need during the night for contacting us about medication.

Mr. Jones phoned the office at 5:00 p.m. and said that things were much better, that Portia had just gotten up and was talking and seemed almost normal. He asked if she should continue with the medication and was informed that she should. He talked at great length about himself and his need for affection from his children which he felt Portia was now beginning to understand. He felt that she had just begun to really love her father. He also needed some assurance that we liked him, and was pleased when given this assurance. He said that Portia could talk on the phone which she did very briefly, indicating that she was feeling better, but without any real conversation. Mr. Jones was told that we would be seeing him and his family the next afternoon and he asked if we could come to his home instead of the family coming into the hospital. When we suggested that we would like to see them in the office, he was agreeable to this.

At 10:00 p.m. that night, Mr. and Mrs. Jones brought Portia to the emergency room, very upset about unusual behavior on her part. There had been church people at their home who had conducted a divine healing service for Portia, though we had taken a stand against these exorcisms. She had also had a very trying phone conversation with her grandmother, and now she was rolling her eyes and tossing her head. The parents were very distressed and quickly brought her to the emergency room. Dr. P. and Mr. F. spoke with the family and relieved their concern, and Dr. P. gave Portia an injection of diphenhydramine. The family then took Portia home.

The late evening emergency room contact was evidence of our availability to the family which is very necessary during the acute phase of the patient's decompensation. The active presence of the Family Treatment Unit enabled the Joneses to cope with the situation. In a small number of cases, the acute phase of the decompensation lingers on and requires this much activity on the part of the Family Treatment Unit. However, in most of the cases, the patient gets over his acute symptoms within twenty-four hours. When this family presented, we failed to fully appreciate the nature of the family problems, and should have done more immediately to find out about the paternal grandmother and her involvement with the family.

The Third Day:

The next morning Miss D. and Mr. F. went to the Jones home and again found Portia asleep. We obtained the additional history from Mrs. Jones that Portia had been under some pressure from her boyfriend in the Navy to make a decision about marrying him. Portia had not felt able to make this decision, in part because she would prefer marrying somebody else. Other history obtained was that the grandmother, to whom Portia had been quite close and upon whom Mr. Jones had been quite dependent, had had cancer for a year and was scheduled for further surgery soon. She and her son had become excessively religious during the past year, and it was this religiosity which had been so very upsetting to Portia the previous night. All the grandmother's friends had been attempting to exorcise devils from her. The visit to the emergency room had been largely motivated by Mrs. Jones' desire to get Portia out of this fanatical atmosphere. Mrs. Jones' move to bring Portia into the emergency room had demonstrated the mother's strength in the situation and how much she was needed as a treatment ally during the acute phase of the girl's symptoms. Of all the Jones family members, the mother appeared to have the least investment in having Portia maintain her symptoms, and was best able to cope rationally with the patient.

In the afternoon the Jones family came to the office forty-five minutes late for their appointment. Portia had been sleeping most of the day and was still noncommunicative. Mr. Jones rambled on for a few minutes as he attempted to apologize for his previous rambling. Mrs. Jones was quite tolerant of his behavior as he discussed some of his own anxieties and the family's concern about Portia. This was a very brief contact and little was accomplished except seeing Mr. Jones somewhat better put together.

The Fifth Day:

On the morning of the fifth day a home visit was made by the research assistant to have the family complete the questionnaires which they had done so far in bits and pieces. With some families, the research aspects of the project can become a bone of contention for a variety of reasons. The Jones family viewed the questionnaires as unnecessary probes into their family system, finding things out about them which they would have preferred to have kept secret.

The Seventh Day:

Two days later Mr. Jones called to inform us that Portia was much better, almost back to normal. A home visit was scheduled for the following day and her medication was reduced from 600 mg. of chlorpromazine a day to 300 mg. a day.

The Eighth Day:

In a morning contact, Miss. D. received a phone call from Mrs. Jones saying that Portia was not doing particularly well, so she and Dr. P. went out on a home visit that afternoon. They found, to the contrary, that Portia was out visiting a friend and was doing quite well. They met her brother Jimmy, and obtained the information from him that the grandmother, Mrs. Jones Sr., was very upsetting to Portia and to everybody else in the family, and that she had been particularly critical of Portia. They set up an appointment for the following day for the entire family.

What had made the about-face from the way Portia was described in the morning to the way she was in the afternoon is hard to explain. Nevertheless, the contact was valuable in that the team got to meet Jimmy, who added further light on the grandmother's significant involvement with the Jones family and in particular, Portia. In retrospect, the grandmother had been mentioned previously as an important figure in the Jones family, but she was not seen as such until now. This undoubtedly was an oversight on our part.

The Ninth Day:

The next day the entire family was seen. Portia was markedly better and said that she had amnesia for the entire period of her illness and remembered only a bad dream in which she came down to a dungeon, a possible reference to the Family Treatment Unit which is located in the basement of the hospital. She expressed the desire to return to work. She looked quite different, was vivacious, attractive, charming, flirtatious. The focus was upon the family's relationship with Mrs. Jones Sr. Mr. Jones did not allow the family to criticize his mother and did not feel very able to handle her himself. Mrs. Jones had somewhat the same relationship with her mother, however, her mother was less of a problem. They encouraged us to see Mrs. Jones Sr. the following day.

The family was obviously very wary of the paternal grandmother. Mr. Jones was frightened of her and fearful that his family would criticize her, which led us to interview Mrs. Jones Sr. apart from the rest of the family. We already had some indication of the interaction between the family and the grandmother and wanted to avoid the unfolding of any conflicts between them for fear that this would be too threatening and damage the relationship with the Family Treatment Unit.

When seen in the office on the tenth day, Mrs. Jones Sr. was a very attractive elderly woman, obviously quite concerned with making a middle-class appearance. She was extremely critical of her daughter-in-law and then denied that she had been. She was obviously still quite overprotective of her son. She had not allowed him to attend school so that she could keep him at home with her and her husband while they traveled. She herself was not allowed to go to school because her mother was afraid that she would be kidnapped. She was quite critical of Portia and expressed great alarm about her sexual activity. She felt it was abnormal for a woman to enjoy sex and felt that Portia was a very bad person, probably mentally retarded, who would come to no good end. She was encouraged to make some effort to patch up her conflicts with her daughter-in-law and to be more encouraging to Portia. Mrs. Jones Sr. was obviously very guilty about her role in Portia's illness.

The main attempt in this interview was to get some understanding of the grandmother and to assess the level of her involvement with the family and Portia. Her obvious moralistic attitude was clear and unshakeable. However, she did express concern over Portia's emotional condition and could appreciate the need to be more accepting and less critical of her granddaughter at this time. We made this kind of appeal to the woman, knowing full well that it was a temporary measure to relieve the pressure on Portia. Unquestionably, the long-standing pattern of interaction between the grandmother and the Jones family was nonamenable to any change within the scope of our emergency treatment approach.

The Sixteenth Day:

Mrs. Jones brought in the three children. Portia would not leave the car until Miss D. and Mr. F. went out and insisted that she do so. She was being very stubborn, pretending not to understand us, and acting in a semicatatonic manner. She was also acting physically sick and it was difficult to determine how much of this was conscious and how much anxiety underlay it. The family did talk about how much better Portia was most of the time and how irritating it was to them when she was acting as she was on this occasion. Portia said that she felt that her major problems were that she did not have anybody she could marry. She wanted to get married and didn't know how to go about doing so since both of her boyfriends were in Viet Nam. She also wanted to get a job and was afraid she would not be hired. The family was encouraged to be quite intolerant of this stubborn, nonresponsive behavior, and to insist that she go ahead and get a job. They were told to take her around to make sure that she made job applications. The family was then informed of the conversation Dr. P. had with Mrs. Jones Sr. and of our belief that she did not have an active cancer at this time. They were advised to investigate this further, and it was interesting to note that Mrs. Jones Sr. had neglected to inform the family of any of this.

The initial part of this interview reflected the aggressive approach of the Family Treatment Unit by going out to the car when Portia refused to come into the interview. Once in the interview, she responded quite well by bringing out her concerns about going steady and marriage. We focused principally on her job situation, encouraging the family to urge her towards work. The essence of our contact with the grandmother was relayed on to the Jones family in order to make them less fearful of her cancer (an obvious ploy on

her part to manipulate and dominate). In reviewing the grandmother's ploy about her cancer to the family, the Family Treatment
Unit was undoubtedly impulsive and did not discuss its revelation
with Mrs. Jones Sr. Retrospectively, we might have been more
careful and given more thought to discussing this with her. The
Jones family accepted this information quite well, showing little
outward emotion or relief about the grandmother's condition, almost
as if this was just another gambit of hers to dominate them.

The Seventeenth Day:

During another office visit, Mr. F. spoke with Portia and her
mother regarding employment possibilities. Role playing was done
in which Mr. F. acted as the interviewer and she as the job appli-
cant since she seemed very uncomfortable about applying for a job.
At times Portia appeared preoccupied and was not responsive to
questions but with a little prodding she did come around. She said
that she was interested in waitress work, baby-sitting, and typing
and was asked to type an article from the local newspaper and
typed several lines which contained a number of mistakes, but was
alert to the mistakes that she made. We then reviewed the Help
Wanted section of the newspaper and she showed interest in applying for waitress work at two restaurants and also agreed to go to
the State Employment Service. The mother was very supportive
and interested in Portia's obtaining employment.

The Eighteenth Day:

The next day Portia phoned that she had applied for a waitress
job at a restaurant. She told them that she had attended high
school and taken courses in being a waitress and now was being
told by her doctor to go to work. She was also going to the State
Employment Service. Mr. F. spoke with Mrs. Jones and stressed
the need for Portia to actively apply for work that day and during
the following week.

Referral—Job Placement—Independent Living Situation

Portia's need for vocational counseling and training by the Department of Vocational Rehabilitation was very apparent. She was
socially backward, and poorly prepared to effectively compete with
people her age in the work world. Since being graduated from high

school, her employment had been limited to protective domestic situations, sanctioned and structured by the grandmother. It was extremely doubtful that she could locate and maintain a job without considerable support from an outside agency. The Joneses accepted the referral and Portia was sent to the Sheltered Workshop. This is a private community agency providing vocational counseling and placement for patients on a contractual basis with the State Department of Vocational Rehabilitation.

Though Portia was referred, the Family Treatment Unit's involvement with her did not stop. The referral is a vital, ongoing process and not the act of shipping the patient off to another agency and then forgetting about her. The Family Treatment Unit makes itself available to the patient, family, and community resource for future crisis consultation.

The importance of working closely with agencies is dramatically seen with Portia's difficulties at the Sheltered Workshop. Many community agencies, unfortunately, have an inherent fear of psychiatric patients. Any of the patient's craziness, peculiar behavior, and uncooperativeness frightens the agency, often providing the basis and excuse to precipitously discharge the patient. Agencies have rules and regulations and by golly the patient must conform, otherwise he is out on his ear. Progress with patients like Portia, however, is very slow, and agency personnel need frequent encouragement and boosting to continue their efforts. Faced with this situation, the referring source must be willing to maintain a continuing active interest.

Through attendance over a year's time at a number of interagency conferences, the Family Treatment Unit passed on significant information and impressions which had been found useful in working with the Jones family. In order for Portia to benefit fully from the workshop, she and her family needed casework services. The family, especially Mrs. Jones needed to be made a close ally to encourage Portia's participation in the program. Also, in working with the family, much of the family's underlying pathologic interaction, such as Portia's sexual feelings towards her father, needed to be avoided. Instead, there should be a reality basis principally focusing on her current adjustment in the home and at the workshop.

Initially, there was much interagency squabbling between the Sheltered Workshop and the Department of Vocational Rehabilitation over who was going to provide casework services for the family. Mr. F. took a mediator role, trying to make sure that Portia did not get lost in the struggle between the two agencies. The workshop provided a full gamut of services to Portia but viewed the family as secondary. The Department caseworker correctly wanted to involve both Portia and the family. The workshop gave the family caseworker a very hard time about setting up times to interview Portia and providing current adjustment information. After much haggling, it was finally decided that the Department worker would see Portia and her family at home and closely communicate with the Workshop person seeing Portia, which worked out fairly well for all concerned.

Portia's adjustment at the Workshop was quite erratic. Initially, there were many absences, tardinesses, and provocative behavior with other patients. The Workshop did not fully appreciate Portia's inadequacy, such as her not knowing which bus to take and the importance of being on time. Until she could begin to do things on her own, the mother needed to be involved as a close ally. Portia sexually teased other patients, and she had to be structured and limited from relating to others in this way. The Workshop was doubtful about what could be done for her, but they agreed after one month to place her on a ninety-day work strengthening program, following which they would reevaluate her situation.

As the Workshop had no psychiatrist immediately available, the Family Treatment Unit agreed to supervise Portia's medication. She was initially placed on 100 mg. of Mellaril q.i.d. There was much communication about the medication as Portia often resisted taking it and dosage adjustments had to be made, as the Workshop felt she was too groggy to function. Communication was maintained with the family caseworker to encourage Mrs. Jones to have Portia take her medicine.

After securing several extensions in time from the Department of Vocational Rehabilitation and contending with much uneven performance from Portia, the Workshop, at the end of ten months, felt that she had made sufficient progress to be placed in an employment situation as a nurse's aide at a nursing home. The family caseworker felt that the Jones family had made some progress, but not sufficient to allow Portia to continue living at home and to be expected to hold on to a job. Portia was provided with a living situation in the home of an elderly widow who took an active interest in her well being. It was quite a struggle for the family to accept Portia's living away from home as they now felt her earnings should go to help support the family. To help the Joneses through this situation, the family caseworker continued counseling with them.

SUMMARY

Portia's behavior and symptoms reflected a struggle for emancipation from her family who had repeatedly frustrated her efforts. She had been truly scapegoated, marked as a "retardate" and unable to function away from the protective environment of her family and grandmother. Portia's anger at these people was not expressed directly, except through her psychotic symptoms.

The point at which Portia made contact with the Family Treatment Unit was when she was at the crossroad between her grandmother and her parents. The grandmother was rejecting her and the parents were condemning her.

Once the Family Treatment Unit was able to help Portia recompensate, the attempt was made to provide her with social and work skills so as to function independently of the family. The usual course of crisis treatment is to help the patient "over the hump" and restore the status quo. However, when this "status quo" is so pathologic for a patient this young, there is an attempt to go further. This is beyond the scope of the Family Treatment Unit's crisis treatment, but requires the efforts of community agencies more appropriate for long-term goals. Nevertheless, as was demonstrated, the Family Treatment Unit needs to play a vital backup and consultative role to these agencies.

The problems of Portia and her family will be wrestled with for a long time, and there will be many reverses and setbacks. Unless the community is willing to make a long-term investment to maintain Portia in her new job and living situation, this plan will be ineffective.

CHAPTER 6

A Caretaker Crisis

Approximately 20 per cent of the families that have been treated by the Family Treatment Unit have been referred for a caretaker crisis. Caretaker crisis may be defined as a situation in which the professional person or institution is in difficulty about the treatment of a patient or family. This may result in a move to either temporarily or permanently terminate the relationship. The Family Treatment Unit perceives the caretaker crisis as being of two different types. The first kind of caretaker crisis is seen less frequently and occurs when a caretaker, after permitting regressive dependency, dismisses a case and makes no further suggestions for treatment. The second type occurs in a long-standing relationship when the caretaker becomes unduly alarmed and seeks help from other sources for his patient. Both types are discussed in some detail with emphasis given the second type of caretaker crisis, as this is the crisis most often dealt with by the Family Treatment Unit.

The first type of caretaker crisis occurs when an agency or institution gets angry at the patient or family. They will discharge the case and refuse readmission when the patient or family once again seeks help from them. The agency will persist in their refusal even when requested to continue by another professional agency to whom the patient has turned as a result of the original agency's termination. An example of this kind of situation was the case of Mrs. Jackson. Mrs. Jackson was initially seen in the Emergency Room of the University of Colorado Medical Center. She presented a history of having been a day patient at a state hospital for the past three years. Two days prior to her seeking assistance at the emergency room, she had been discharged from the state hospital. The patient was in a highly anxious state, demanding medications which had been discontinued at the time of her discharge from the state hospital. She was diagnosed in the emergency room as a pseudoneurotic schizophrenic. She and her husband fell into the Family Treatment Unit sample. True to the quick assessment procedure of the Family Treatment Unit, an interview with the identified patient and husband was held immediately. Mrs. Jackson, for the past eight years, had been addicted to various tranquillizers and sedatives. This addiction began while she and her husband were stationed in Italy where she developed asthma and began taking these medicines for relief. Though the asthma ceased, she continued with the drugs. Her household functioning was negligible but the family tolerated this lack of functioning well so long as she was a day patient at the state hospital. There were four children and the two elder children and Mr. Jackson, along with Mrs. Jackson's parents, ran the household. After listening to the Jacksons' story, it was clear that the Jacksons' situation was a chronic one and the present crisis was a direct result of the discharge from the state hospital two days previously. A call was then made to the state hospital treatment team leader, a psychiatrist. The Family Treatment Unit's psychiatrist explained his views of the present difficulty and asked if the state facility could continue seeing the patient. This was suggested as an alternative to an unnecessary acute hospitalization at a different facility necessitating new history taking, new psychologic testing, new therapeutic relationship, etc. The state hospital psychiatrist indicated that the patient had been coming to the day hospital three days a week instead of five days a week as the hospital team felt she should. She was therefore, after due notice, discharged as not cooperating with the hospital program. Furthermore, the team psychiatrist stated that if the Family Treatment Unit persisted in having the patient reevaluated for possible readmission, the team would have to go through the motions but would exercise their perogative of refusing admission. The Family Treatment Unit had on choice but to treat the case.

A multiplicity of agencies are now engaged in mental health activities. They may be working with patients or families in a counseling situation, in school settings, public health settings, community mental health clinics and hospitals. Varying theoretical frameworks, agency policies, individual caretaker concerns and a multiplicty of other factors determine how agencies or institutions deal with the mental health problems of the people they see. The caretaker crisis that has been observed most frequently in the Family Treatment

Unit setting occurs when the caretaking agency panics or feels that they are unable to cope with a problem presented them by a family or patient. This panic may occur when a weekend is coming up and the caretaker will not be available. Feeling this inability, the caretaker often times refers the case to the emergency room of the hospital. When the Family Treatment Unit begins to see a family, a quick assessment of the involvement of the caretaking agency is made. We look to see if the caretaking agency has made some move toward continuing with the case after acute treatment is over. In the latter category we have noted that often caretakers will phone the emergency room and explain to the emergency room resident their perceptions of the problem for which they've referred the person. This is indicative of their concern and involvement. On the Family Treatment Unit's part, we contact the caretaking agency as quickly as possible. We ask that the caretaker become involved in our crisis treatment if they would like to be. The Family Treatment Unit indicates our temporary responsibility for helping the family cope with the crisis and our continuing responsibility in a consultant capacity for assisting the caretaker in reassuming a treatment relationship with the patient or family. As an agency working with crisis situations, we find developing close relationships and utilizing already developed caretaker relationships a vital part of our crisis management.

A clinical illustration of this type of caretaker crisis and how the Family Treatment Unit dealt with it will best exemplify the points previously expressed.

On June 9, 1966 at 10:30 p.m. the Family Treatment Unit accepted the Little family from the Emergency Psychiatric Service. Mrs. Little, the identified patient, had been seen on an outpatient basis for the past two days and was now deemed admissible to the hospital according to the resident psychiatrist. The resident stated that the patient presented "a very pathologic unstable history often hard to follow—though no evidence of thought disorder. Is afraid she may batter five year old. Is afraid she may run away from it all—possibly suicide—is depressed." The resident felt she needed to be hospitalized immediately. Her diagnosis was given as "an emotionally unstable personality with associated depression and anxiety." She had originally been referred to the Emergency Psychiatric Service for evaluation on a voluntary basis by a psychiatric social worker from one of the local mental health clinics.

Mrs. Little is a white woman, 23 years old and married five years. Her early history was obtained from the emergency room note and the resumes of previous hospitalizations at CPH.

Mrs. Little came from a large family who lived in Colorado. She has four sisters and two brothers. Her mother died at age 42 of uremic poisoning associated with toxemia of pregnancy. Mrs. Little's father is sixty-one and still living. According to the historical information, Mrs. Little's father attempted to rape her when she was twelve and this began a long series of episodes in which she ran away from home. This running away culminated in the patient being placed in a state home for girls. She ran away from the state home, was raped by a man she had dated for a week and became pregnant. The baby was placed for adoption. Following this episode, Mrs. Little became a nurses' aide in a nursing home. She met her husband who was stationed at an Air Force base in Denver. They were married, spent a month's leave at his parents' home, and then went to live at an Air Force base. The precipitating events are unclear, but in March of that year Mr. Little became psychotic and was hospitalized at an Air Force hospital in California. At approximately the same time, Mrs. Little was hospitalized at an Air Force facility in Idaho and then transferred to a state hospital in that state. She was viewed as having an hysterical personality with schizophrenic features. The note also states she was a poor socializer and a pathologic liar. It was discovered during this two month hospitalization that Mrs. Little was three months' pregnant. The patient was discharged on Prochlorperazine. Mr. Little was discharged from the Air Force for psychiatric reasons in June of 1961. The family returned to Denver and their son was born in October. Mr. Little held four jobs in the first two years following Air Force discharge. He had difficulty in relating to his bosses. He had a more stable job in 1966 as an automobile mechanic in spite of the fact that he had two psychiatric admissions in 1965. His diagnosis was schizophrenic reaction with depression. According to his hospital resumes, there had been increasing financial worries, nervousness and depression.

During Mr. Little's last hospitalization in Colorado Psychiatric Hospital, Mrs. Little was referred to a local mental health clinic where she began receiving treatment six months prior to coming to the emergency room. During her husband's hospitalization, a great deal of work was done directly with Mrs. Green, the Social Worker who had been working with Mrs. Little. Four months after the crisis work we reviewed the course of events in an interview with Mrs. Green—an interview which was recorded and transcribed. Certain relevant portions of that interview are utilized here for clarification of the process of caretaker crisis management.

"I had been working with her and with the boy over a period of time. They were inconsistent with their visits, they'd come occasionally and a lot of times they wouldn't show or they would call and cancel. And it seemed like the more upset she was, the less likely she was to come in for her interviews. You could tell this over the phone and very often she would want to talk, which very often I did because, you know, on previous occasions she had done things like call me and tell me she had taken medication or something and couldn't come to the clinic because she was sick and she'd say that she felt so dizzy and I really felt like I had to talk to her over the phone because I was kind of worried about her—she sounded like she was getting further and further away. However, that hadn't been going on just then, but she had been missing her visits and calling up, upset, and as I recall, her visits were supposed to be on Monday and she missed that week. I believe she had also called the previous weekend because we were experimenting with a telephone secretary. Prior to that we weren't offering twenty-four hour service. We were curious how many calls were coming in over the weekend that we weren't getting, and this was a little experiment—she was the only one that called. Then as the week went by, she kept calling every day, more and more upset. I tried to get her into the office but she had all these excuses why she couldn't come. Usually they related to her husband having the car, or she was too sick, or her husband didn't want her to come. She was angry at her husband as I remember, and as I recall, she was feeling very upset because she had been involved with another man to some extent. She was angry at her husband because he didn't seem able to accept this other man very comfortably. She thought it would be nice if the other man could come to the house and the three of them could sit down and talk. And of course, she was being a little unrealistic about this to say the least. She had talked with me before about the affair with the other man, and had seemed to feel rather guilty about it although I don't know if this was bona-fide guilt or not. The other man had gotten in trouble, had been in jail, and had gotten out and was making demands on her. He wanted to come out and borrow money as I recall, I don't know, I've forgotten some of the details. But, at any rate, she was caught between her husband and the other man at this point. She was getting more and more anxious, and she called, she was having all kinds of symptoms."

The caretaker attempted unsuccessfully to get Mrs. Little to come into the office. Mrs. Little continued to call and the social worker, realizing the weekend was coming up when she was unavailable to the patient, became increasingly concerned as evidenced by the following.

MISS D.Y.—When was it that you decided to send her into the emergency room?

SOCIAL WORKER—Well, all week long I kept trying to get her to come into the office. She was obviously, at least my feeling after listening to her on the phone was that she was becoming more and more anxious, and I thought that if I could just get her in, I could understand this better rather than fragmented telephone conversations. But I wasn't successful in getting her in, and I kept feeling this increased anxiety on her part. She kept talking about wanting to go to the hospital, and I kept on trying to get her to come in.

MISS D.Y.—To the hospital?

SOCIAL WORKER—No, in to see me. And this went on until Friday, at which point *I really was rather concerned about her, and I wasn't going to be there in the clinic anymore and we don't have an emergency service and I really think that she didn't want outpatient help at that point and was really kind of desperate.*

MISS D.Y.—So would you say, just from your point of view because you weren't going to be there over the weekend and had this patient who was very anxious, the resource that seemed most feasible to you was—

SOCIAL WORKER—Well, now also this woman had made a suicide attempt in the past, and I don't think I necessarily felt that she would go and commit suicide, but I thought, knowing Mrs. Little, that she could do some really strange things when she really became anxious and that she was sort of telling me in lots of ways that she thought she was losing control of herself. And that she didn't know what was going to happen. *Admittedly, I was getting a little anxious about this too, for you see my weekend was coming up and I wouldn't be available to her and she had been talking hospital for a day or two. So finally I said to her, 'Mrs. Little, if you are feeing this anxious and feel that you need to see somebody to help you decide what to do, why don't you go to the hospital and talk to somebody in the emergency room'.* I did call however, and I did call Mr. Howland so that in the event that she were hospitalized, a foster home could be arranged temporarily for their youngster. And I talked to her husband about taking her after I finally, myself, accepted the fact that maybe this had to happen.

The social worker did not just turn the case over to the hospital and remove herself from the situation. She attempted to arrange for foster home placement for the boy if need be, transportation to the hospital for the patient, and then talked to the emergency room resident.

So Mrs. Little arrived at the emergency room and was seen by a psychiatric resident and as previously mentioned, was deemed admissible to the hospital. According to the admission note, Mrs. Little came to the hospital accompanied by her husband.

The Family Treatment Unit was contacted as the case met our criteria, was randomly selected, and we took over at 10:30 p.m. A brief joint interview was conducted. The information obtained was that Mrs. Little was feeling unable to control her impulses and feared she might harm her child or run away from the home situation. She felt her four year old boy was uncontrollable. Mrs. Little insisted that she received no help from the mental health clinic. Mr. Little during this session was quiet but did state that he himself had been hospitalized twice in the year but now had a good job which he wanted to keep. Both the Littles wanted Mrs. Little hospitalized, but it was noted that the more Mrs. Little talked about her situation, though she looked physically tired, the less she showed the anxiety which she had presented at the emergency room. An agreement was reached for the Littles to return home and then come to the Family Treatment Unit's offices in the morning with their son.

The next morning the Family Treatment Unit's nurse and social worker met with the family. The Family Treatment Unit team psychiatrist observed the interview behind the one-way screen. The

interview was concerned primarily with the problem the Littles
presented, the inability of the couple to communicate with each
other over issues regarding the care of the small boy and finances.
It was noted that when Mrs. Little did not get her way she began
to scream, threatening to kill herself or run away from the house.
Mr. Little felt unable to handle his wife and retreated completely
from the situation by cowering in his room. Mr. Little appeared
to have completely given up attempting to do anything about the
situation. This seemed especially noticeable regarding the four year
old son. The child, who was present during the interview, seemed
limited verbally, more so than most children his age. He was a disturbed youngster who had become the pawn for his parents' battles.
The couple consistently differed about the handling of the child
and Mrs. Little felt that she received no support from her husband
in her attempts to control him. The couple was also in much conflict over financial matters. Mr. Little had turned over the handling
of the finances to Mrs. Little. She felt that he used her handling of
the money as a means to criticize her and would have liked to return the finances to her husband. In the joint interview it was observed that Mrs. Little seemed to verbally dominate the couple.
Mr. Little needed a lot of prodding and support to express his point
of view. The final note of this particular interview was that Mrs.
Little appeared much better, showing none of the psychiatric symptoms which brought about her referral to the Emergency Room. A
home visit was arranged for the next day.

The Family Treatment Unit team social worker contacted Mrs.
Little's clinic social worker, Mrs. Green, to inform her of the Family
Treatment Unit's presence in the case. The clinic social worker
appeared completely frustrated in trying to "handle" Mrs. Little
and the four year old child. She had met Mr. Little once, at intake,
about six months before her referral. Mrs. Green explained her perceptions of the events which led to the request for hospitalization in
much the same terms as were previously quoted. An explanation of
the workings of the Family Treatment Unit was given over the
phone. In addition, a request for a joint meeting was made and
readily accepted by the clinic social worker.

MISS D.Y.—We first contacted you—it must have been the day after the
night she was admitted to the project. What did you think when we
contacted you? Your initial impression?

SOCIAL WORKER—I don't think I knew enough about your team at that point. However, I was glad that Mrs. Little could be kept out of the hospital because this is really never a permanent solution to anything. I guess I wondered how you did it in a way.

MISS D.Y.—Did you feel we gave you a good explanation? What do you recall? What was your—

SOCIAL WORKER—It's really hard to remember back. Your team social worker called me and explained a little about the team and of course, I was interested—I'd heard a little about it. And he said that you were coming out. I don't remember any particular reactions, I mean I was real glad that you were coming out.

The referring caretaker appeared to be genuinely relieved that the hospitalization was avoided and that active intervention was provided. She also seemed curious about our team and our methods of treatment. The clinic social worker was asked to join the team in active treatment but she was unable to come to our offices. Instead, the team asked to meet with her at the clinic.

Extending the team not only to the patient and family, but to caretakers as well is an integral part of our method of treatment. The caretaker was made to feel a part of the crisis treatment, as indeed she was. One concern may be for the caretaker's feelings. Will he be likely to feel that he has made a mistake? Worse yet, is his professional judgment in error? This need not be the case. Crisis treatment can be anxiety provoking for the professional person who is not familiar with its technics. New methods of treatment need to be explained in an atmosphere of respect for the caretaker. Placing another professional in a position of defensiveness rarely accomplishes learning or for that matter, cooperation. To further illustrate our workings in the Little case, the following excerpts of our interview with the caretaker are offered:

MISS D.Y.—When we came out and talked with you, what was your impression then on what we were saying about the case? Did you look at any other alternatives?

SOCIAL WORKER—Well, to me it was extremely helpful because I think that—I think it helped me to re-assess Mrs. Little a bit. In a way it embarrassed me a little because I hadn't seen some of the things before that the team saw so quickly—really.

MISS D.Y.—Uh-huh.

SOCIAL WORKER—Because usually when I work with someone like Mrs. Little, I'd think I'd be a little more alert to the fact that she needed more direction, more structuring, than all that I had been offering. Although I had tried not to let her regress, or in content, in all previous interviews, but I had let her, probably—probably I hadn't been just as directive as would be best in their case.

MISS D.Y.—Uh-huh, I think this is probably what we recommended.

SOCIAL WORKER—Yes, more direct interpretations about how she was getting herself into these messes. Well, I think perhaps the crisis team, both in skill and opportunity too—to see the family together and all, and to see them in their home—really had a better perception of what was going on than I had. I don't think I could have made these interpretations as well before because I don't think I really saw it as clearly.

MISS D.Y.—And you had been seeing her for—

SOCIAL WORKER—Oh off and on. I saw her husband and her too for a joint interview—but he wouldn't stick at all—he was too scared.

MISS D.Y.—Yes.

SOCIAL WORKER—Its interesting now that I think back. She came to us too, under a great deal of pressure—wanting immediate help and talked to us over the phone, and we tried to get her to get on our wait list. We aren't in a position to make very many exceptions but when I talked to her over the phone, when she came in—and she kept talking about this child—I could tell really that her anxiety was at such a level that it wasn't just the child—that something was going on, and she sounded to me like she was having an acute anxiety. I remember telling the clinic psychiatrist that I would feel better if I could at least get her in and find out what this was all about and then, if it was something appropriate, we could put her back on the waiting list, but if it was something else, maybe it was something that needed looking into a little earlier. So I guess she does get people feeling—

MISS D.Y.—A little panicky?

SOCIAL WORKER—Well—that they ought to meet her needs immediately which, of course, fits in with her impulsiveness.

During the first office interview with the Littles, a home visit was scheduled for later that afternoon. In situations of crisis we have found that a home visit within twenty-four hours of initiating treatment aids in assessment of the crisis.

The team nurse and social worker visited the home of the Littles. The Littles resided in the city of Golden close to the center of town.

They had a pleasant two bedroom basement apartment which was neatly and adequately furnished. The little boy was sleeping, and Mr. Little had gone on to work. It was noted that Mrs. Little appeared comfortable in her home and seemed to enjoy having the team visit her. Most of the discussion at the time of this visit was of a history-getting nature. The home visit pointed up the great need of Mrs. Little to ventilate about her situation which relieved it somewhat. However, a considerable amount of structuring and direction was felt necessary in any kind of treatment relationship with her.

Following the home visit there were numerous phone calls between Mrs. Little and the team social worker for the next two days. Efforts were made to set up an interview with Mr. Little. He had expressed the belief that the treatment team was siding with Mrs. Little, especially since she had been seen at home without him. Mr. Little cancelled one appointment and then the team arranged to see him at his place of business. This, he also refused. Mrs. Little was apparently provoking her husband to the point where on the fourth evening after the case began, Mr. Little threatened his wife and child with a gun. Mrs. Little then called the police and a local psychiatrist who had previously cared for Mr. Little. The psychiatrist wanted to have Mr. Little hospitalized. This made him furious, and he retaliated by stating he would divorce his wife and also commit *her* to a hospital. Through phone conversations, the team social worker was able to calm Mr. Little down and reassure him that the Family Treatment Unit was in no way trying to shanghai him into the hospital. The team social worker also told him that we were trying to work with the two of them regarding the marriage problem.

To summarize the case so far, the Littles were a couple who engaged in very destructive and provocative behavior with a scapegoat and victim being the four year old son. Whenever a situation became stressful, Mr. and Mrs. Little retreated from each other by running away or entering a hospital. A great deal of the problem in trying to treat the Littles was the use of the individual approach to the family situation, as Mrs. Little had used her therapy sessions with the clinic social worker as a weapon against her husband. He, in turn, became very furious, retreated, and refused to engage in any kind of constructive interaction with his wife. The Family

Treatment team had been most effective with the couple when the team was directive in telling them to cease destroying each other and begin to be more attentive to one another's needs. This was done by telling Mrs. Little over the phone to make sure she had the house orderly and her husband's meal prepared when he came home from work. Mr. Little was told to begin facing up to his wife and to stop retreating to his bedroom or considering divorce. In addition, the clinic social worker was kept appraised of the methods that the team was employing and an appointment was set up for Mrs. Little to meet with the social worker at her office within one week after the caretaker's initial referral to the hospital.

The team felt that close consultation would have to be carried out with the county clinic and a clear understanding made that the team would be available for subsequent crises. This family was viewed as a volatile one but one that could be dealt with on an outpatient level if the caretaker would be willing. A visit was made by the entire Family Treatment Unit team to the clinic social worker in her office. We reviewed our contacts with the Littles and the clinic social worker did likewise. She felt that possibly she had not fully appreciated the nature of the problems in the Little family and seemed very receptive to the team's suggestions. Mrs. Little did keep the appointment that the team set up for her with the clinic social worker.

The interview that was conducted with the clinic social worker some months after this meeting revealed the following information.

MISS D.Y.—How do you feel that, in the long run, the case has gone? You know—looking back at the pre-crisis stuff and the crisis, and now after—

SOCIAL WORKER—Well, I think I can only speculate. She has been in a few times since then. She does seem, on the whole, much less depressed. I don't think I have really followed it consistently enough to honestly say whether or not there has been lasting progress or that she— achieved new ways of handling things.

MISS D.Y.—Well, that is almost an impossible goal. How about your reaction to some of the things that she may be throwing out—if she were to have another crisis again or would seem to—

SOCIAL WORKER—Well—if she again seemed to have this mounting anxiety, I would use structuring, I would try again to get her in the office, but you know, if you can't you can't. I'd feel a little less anxious about myself, because I'd know that in the back of my mind here was this team who knew this family and who was interested, and I would call you probably and let you know what was going on and see if you had any ideas that I might put into effect and if you didn't, maybe you would want to look in on her again. Would that be appropriate?

MISS D.Y.—Sure that would be appropriate. We offer ourselves as active consultants—however you would like it.

SOCIAL WORKER—I haven't been too successful in any contacts with the husband. And she doesn't want me to be either.

MISS D.Y.—No.

SOCIAL WORKER—I have called him a time or two, but she is always saying that this disturbs him, that this really makes him mad to have people call him at work. I think with Mrs. Little and her husband, the best we can ever expect—I don't think we'll ever close the case. I think they have a marriage of sorts that has some kind of neurotic, almost psychotic, things that they give to each other, that I think they probably need, but at the same time, they continually mutilate each other. I don't think they could live apart—but they really don't live too well together either. Of course, I worry about the boy.

MISS D.Y.—Is he starting to school yet?

SOCIAL WORKER—She has him enrolled now in a preschool in Denver, not every day, which would be better for her. It was shortly after she was out here, it was during the summer I guess, that she got very upset and told me that she was afraid that she was going to kill him. What she wanted at that time was if I know any resources where she could put him for the day and because she thought things would just be wrong if she had to be with him all the time—and I would agree. Unfortunately, we don't have much of this in Jefferson Co. (places I mean). And when they moved to Denver, she was able to find someplace. She was going all over—up to Golden, I think she even went down and talked to somebody at Headstart—which might not be too bad an idea for this kid.

MISS D.Y.—Well it sounds like she was using your services appropriately, and you were giving her support to go ahead and do what she—

SOCIAL WORKER—Well, I think it's better for her—she can at least now say, "This kid and I are better off if we just don't spend so much time together." This is a little different than the way it used to be where she used to feel so bound up and so guilty about her actions toward the youngster. She couldn't really accept this kind of toleration.

MISS D.Y.—I think you've done a very fine job. These are very difficult people to handle. The most difficult probably—this kind of a manipulative impulsive person.

SOCIAL WORKER—Yes—I have an idea that the reason I haven't been hearing from her so much—now she did call me at one point and wanted to start therapy for the boy again, and I was never really able exactly to understand what kind of anxiety this was. And we did start, but again, at this point, it's that if she wants to come in—call me.

MISS D.Y.—As you said, she's probably somebody that will call up periodically and you'll never close your books.

SOCIAL WORKER—No, and I think, you see—I used to think in terms of offering her support because I think that the goals were awfully limited anyway, but at this point I think that as a result of your contact and our conference, I'm thinking more in terms of offering her support and direction. Which I could beat myself on the head for not having seen before, because, I think her contacts are going to be brief anyway. She's not going to stick to a scheduled interview plan and she just gets so frightened and so confused that she doesn't know what she is to do, and she just needs someone to tell her what to do and she can go home and do it—you know.

The steps that were followed in dealing with the caretaker crisis were:
1. Assessing the kind and degree of caretaker involvement in the crisis.
2. Enlisting the assistance of the caretaker in the crisis management or getting his cooperation for our crisis intervention.
3. Sharing by person to person or close telephone contacts the ongoing results of crisis intervention.
4. Referral back to the original caretaker, if this is possible.
5. Offering real and active availability to the caretaker whenever the caretaker requires assistance.

The relationship between the Family Treatment Unit and the caretaker involved in the previous presentation had many positive results. It enabled the caretaker to objectively evaluate her participation in the crisis leading to the request for hospitalization. The consultation and support allowed her room to look at other means of dealing with the situation and others similar to it. Furthermore, she was able to put it to good use in subsequent contacts. Hopefully, she could also share her learning with other clinic caretakers. The relationship also established a liaison, which is useful in referrals, between the Family Treatment Unit and the county clinic.

CHAPTER 7

Crisis in a "Doll's House" Family

A family may be said to be in crisis when its usual means of handling change prove insufficient—when it has to resort to the more "drastic" and public of the measures normally available for coping with change. A crisis is therefore a type of reaction on the part of a family; it is not, for example, a set of hazardous external events, nor is it a mere upset in the family equilibrium: some families can handle both external and internal upsets within their own confines and with competence. With such a definition of the term "crisis," it becomes apparent that there exists a continuum of contributions to this event—that a crisis may be produced primarily by external events, primarily by internal stresses, or by some combination of the two. It is a curious feature of the families of people seeking hospitalization at Colorado Psychiatric Hospital, however, that they are very seldom, if ever, overwhelmed by events in outer reality without a significant contribution of intrafamilial pathology. In the three cases described so far, the contribution of long-standing patterns to the crisis which led one member to request hospitalization is quite evident. In the case to be described in this chapter, such contribution is primary. It may be said that this case typifies one end of the continuum we have just described, in that the crisis seems to be generated almost predictably by the family structure itself. Other family types also generate crises primarily from within, but the "Doll's House" is a strikingly clear example of one of the types.

The doll's house situation is one in which the wife is dependent and infantile, and in which the husband's self-esteem and fragile maturity depend on keeping her that way. In such a marriage (which may or may not have children) each of the partners is permitted only a very narrow range of behavior, departures from which may create crises of considerable magnitude. For an upset to occur to the usual equilibrium, it may suffice for one member to change his behavior; no events from the outside are needed for decompensation of one or more members to come about. Thus, typically, the wife may indicate a desire for greater independence and thereby pose a strong threat to her husband's sense of competence and masculinity; the husband may be unable to permit what she wishes, and the ensuing maneuvers may lead to one member's decompensation. It is interesting to note that the decompensating member may be either husband or wife; in spite of the family's usual definition of the wife as the weak member, it is clear, if only from seeing who decompensates, that each partner is "weak" in his own way.

In the case presented in this chapter, the doll's house aspect of the relation between the husband and wife was not immediately apparent. For that reason, the means to be employed by the therapists in their crisis intervention were also unclear. The treatment and the steps required to gather a sufficient understanding of the family dynamics will be described in chronological order; in this manner, hopefully, the connection between the usual family interaction and the crisis will become clear, as will the necessity for intervening not only at the level of the crisis but in the long term patterns themselves.

Three people presented themselves at the emergency room of Colorado General Hospital: Mr. and Mrs. Carver, both in their middle thirties, and Mrs. Russell, Mrs. Carver's mother. They had sought admission for Mrs. Carver and obtained it from the emergency room, but they had fit FTU's criteria for family treatment and were accepted on the usual random basis. Mrs. Carver was very groggy and mute; the only introduction to their difficulty was provided by the admitting physician's note, which said in part:

This married mother of one child was brought in by her husband because of her self-destructive and paranoid ideas. The husband describes the acute onset of the psychosis on (the preceding day) while (the family) was visiting his mother in (a neighboring state). The husband had noticed the patient was somewhat restless before they left and that there was a decrease in her appetite . . . (Yesterday) the patient was talking about selling their house and leaving Denver, and jumped to talking about husband being against her; then got off on a "religious kick." Became violent, tearing down drapes and venetian blinds. Grabbed paring knife and attempted to cut wrists. Family called doctor, who gave her chlorpromazine. Husband brought her back here for treatment . . . The patient is very negativistic, vague, evasive, and won't talk about the problem. Denies most of her problems, just insists that she needs to have a lawyer to divorce her husband. Impression: schizophrenic reaction, schizoaffective.

Dr. M. (Psychologist) and Mr. F. (Social Worker) decided to treat the case together. Even before talking with the family at great length we had formed these impressions: Mr. Carver and Mrs. Russell were presenting a calm, competent and concerned exterior; Mrs. Carver was clearly oversedated; there had been recent contact with part of the extended family, which lived far enough away for us to suspect that the contacts were rare and that therefore the contact had been one of the precipitants of the crisis; Mrs. Carver had made a suicide gesture in the presence of her whole family and was therefore attempting to communicate something by an act that was impossible to say in words (or prohibited from being said). Such impressions formed our starting point, as they do in most cases. In the first interview we hoped to obtain the family's understanding of the difficulties (including, very importantly, the "patient's" understanding of them), and to reconstruct as exactly as we could the sequence of events that had led to the request for hospitalization. In addition, we had hoped to form an impression of the family's usual level of functioning, in order to decide how high the aims of our crisis intervention should be. We accomplished somewhat less, however, mostly because of Mrs. Carver's refusal (and partial inability) to talk. This refusal made it impossible for us to treat the problem as a family problem rather than an individual one; as long as Mrs. Carver did not speak and the family spoke for her, the usual distinction "patient—concerned family" could not be tackled.

In the initial visit we found that for the past several weeks the patient had been very restless and depressed. Mr. Carver had thought it would do his wife good to visit with his folks in the neighboring state; but while visiting there, Mrs. Carver became hysterical, made a suicide gesture by slashing her wrists, and the husband felt the need to return her home. The family had traveled all night in order to get medical attention for Mrs. Carver in Denver. In the neighboring state, Mrs. Carver received a chlorpromazine injection and suppositories from a local physician. She now talked very little, claiming that she was very groggy from the injection, and wanted to go home. Both the husband and Mrs. Russell hovered over her and kept reminding her that she should speak up if she wanted help from the therapists. Mrs. Carver finally said that she had never wanted to make the trip to the neighboring state and that she would have preferred to remain in Denver. Both her husband and Mrs. Russell denied this, saying that Mrs. Carver had wanted to go from the very beginning of her upset. The only important bit of information revealed during this initial interview seemed to be the fact that up until about four years previously Mrs. Russell had been living with the Carvers and their five year old son John. Mrs. Carver had enjoyed the company of her mother, since her husband was self-employed and away a good part of each evening, not to mention the day. She seemed to get worse from the time that her mother left. About two years before, she was hospitalized briefly at a local hospital with a "deep depression" but was unable to elaborate on the hospitalization or her feelings at the time any further. Mr. Carver had a very correct and polite manner about him, seemed protective of his wife and denied that there were marital problems between the two of them. He expressed repeated interest in her happiness and well-being, but was unable to add much to our understanding of the situation. Mrs. Russell did admit that she had been a very close companion of her daughter during the time she lived in her home, but since then had remarried and now had a job of her own; her contacts with her daughter were still daily, but mostly over the telephone. At the end of this initial interview, Dr. P. (psychiatrist) prescribed 150 mg. spansules of chlorpromazine to be taken twice daily, and the therapists arranged a home visit for the following morning.

It is usual for the Family Treatment Unit to have formed a more definite impression of the precipitants of the crisis and of the manner in which chronic pathology may be interacting with it; here our information was more limited. Aside from a refinement of some of the initial impressions, we had discovered what appeared to be too great a closeness between Mrs. Carver and her mother, but we were unable to see what role, if any, it played in the present crisis; we noticed Mr. Carver's and Mrs. Russell's controlling protectiveness, but were unable to judge its role either; and we noted the husband's denial of any marital difficulties, but could not decide to what extent we could afford to question the denial. Tentatively, we were beginning to believe that there was an interplay between the precipitating (and indeed precipitate) visit to the husband's relatives and the chronic difficulties between Mr. and Mrs. Carver (implied in the admitting physician's note), but our information was far from definite. That Mrs. Carver attempted to slash her wrists while visiting her husband's relatives (rather than her own, with whom she got along well) spoke for strong hostility against them—and him, too. But his solicitousness and desire to help were so pervasive that it was difficult to see just what the object of her anger was, unless it was the protectiveness itself.

Now it is also usual for the FTU to be able to direct the family into some activity which interferes with regression by encouraging functioning; family members who complain of being unable to perform certain tasks are encouraged to do so—as are members who do not complain themselves but receive such complaints. In fact, we reverse the equation that families usually present—that they will begin functioning as soon as they feel better—by pointing out that they will feel better as soon as they have begun to function. This may be too simple a way to state the matter, but it has the support of some experience in the prevention of regression—experience which is not universally successful, but very often so. But with the Carver family, such an attempt was difficult at the end of the first hour: the only nonfunctioning member was Mrs. Carver, and she was suffering from heavy sedation; in addition, she appeared to mistrust us in the same manner as she did her husband, perhaps afraid of the control we might exercise over her.

We were confident we could accomplish considerably more in the second interview, which was conducted in the home. For the FTU, it is standard practice to make a home visit for the second interview; it provides information on the manner in which the home territory is divided and shared, but more importantly, it allows the family to show its strengths, as opposed to the weaknesses for which there is every opportunity when on the foreign territory of the psychiatrist's office. The family can play host and offer coffee, and although it is still a "patient," it is less of one. (It would be ingenuous, however, to deny the professional status of the one party and the client status of the other; attempts to do so in certain therapeutic settings are unconvincing to those being treated. The

FTU attempts to make it clear that it offers help, and that in order to be helped a family must cooperate in certain ways.) We expected therefore to find Mrs. Carver more talkative and at ease.

On the following day, therefore, we made a home visit at 8:30 in the morning. The Carvers were living in a very pleasant residential area and the houses seemed to be well kept up. Both Mr. and Mrs. Carver said that they had slept very well the night before and Mrs. Carver looked considerably better. We met with John, who was a sprightly young lad, and he greeted us very warmly. We noted that on the trip back from the neighboring state, Mr. Carver brought along his mother and a friend of hers in order to handle Mrs. Carver. The mother and the friend were supposed to return home later on in the week, but it was unclear just how disruptive the visit was (especially to Mrs. Carver) and what pressure, if any, was being applied on the visitors to leave. They were not there for the interview and apparently stayed in their bedroom; we did not see them throughout the entire interview. Mrs. Carver was very anxious throughout and was very evasive in her conversation. She felt ill at ease, frequently getting up from her chair and changing her dress and going into the kitchen, and mostly didn't want to talk with us at all.

There was some discussion about Mrs. Carver's concern about John's not developing normally. She asked her husband several times whether John played normally with the other boys. She seemed very protective of him, but he, surprisingly, looked to be a very aggressive five year old whose development seemed quite normal. We tried to reassure Mrs. Carver that she was doing a good job with her child; but this seemed to have very little effect on her. Mrs. Carver then expressed some concern about staying around the house too much and said she hoped to find a job. The preceding week, her husband had taken her down to the State Employment Service to make several job applications but it was obvious in this interview that he would rather she did not work outside at all. Instead, he would prefer her to work with him in his business (without pay), a business he had started about two years before. Formerly he had had similar work but as an employee, and made about $7,000 a year; currently he was earning about $300 a month. Mrs. Carver felt that the business was making her husband spend too much time away from her and that in addition, it caused some financial problems. Mrs. Carver had been used to having more money in the past, but because of Mr. Carver's new position, the family's finances were tight.

While Mrs. Carver was in the kitchen, Mr. Carver mentioned to us that his wife had been hospitalized earlier at a local hospital and that she had resented it. She had felt that she was behind bars and since then she had seen no professional person for any further treatment.

The interview proceeded all in all in a very scattered and shotgun fashion. Mrs. Carver communicated very few of her concerns and resisted giving any history. For his part, Mr. Carver talked in very polite terms but denied that there were any problems, claiming that he got along very well with his wife and all her relatives, just as his wife got along very well with his mother. From all that could be gathered, the basic problem appeared to be that Mrs. Carver felt very much hemmed in by all the people who constantly followed her about to make sure she didn't do anything out of the ordinary. She seemed to have lived a very sheltered and protected life, even during a good part of the early years of her marriage, when her mother lived with the young couple.

The efforts of the second day were, therefore, not marked by much apparent success in our understanding the issues and being able to act on them. But as will become clearer later, the communication impasse we thought we had reached at the time was not so total as it appeared; the disappointment we felt reflected rather the expectation experience had led us to form of being able to alleviate the crisis quickly or not at all. The interview did communicate, we believe, that we had three current concerns: to support Mrs. Carver in her self conception as a mother, to air members' dissatisfactions with the strait financial circumstances of the family, and to bring into the open Mrs. Carver's fenced in feelings. The latter in particular tended to become the central focus, but for a discussion of it to be effective, it was necessary to find concrete instances where it had taken place. The most immediate instance seemed to be that of Mrs. Carver's attempts to obtain employment and her husband's calmly but nonetheless definitively uttered suggestion that she work for him instead. We thought it indispensable to support Mrs. Carver in her small move toward independence, and attempted to make the idea acceptable to her husband by not allowing it to become too threatening. Although it is not apparent in the summary of the second hour, our strategy was to appeal to Mr. Carver's self conception as one who is benevolently concerned about his wife, and while reassuring him of our belief in his concern, to enable him to accept permissiveness as one expression of that concern.

After the second interview, we thought it best next time to see the husband and wife separately; Mrs. Carver, aside from being reluctant to talk to anyone, seemed particularly so in front of her husband. We had by this time formed some notion of what might and might not be accomplished with this family, and decided to make our goals clear to the Carvers in one further visit with them. Our goals were very similar but the technics by which we would attempt to achieve them with each individual separately had to differ.

On the third day, therefore, Dr. M. saw Mrs. Carver, while Mr. F. interviewed her husband. Before the visit, however, Mr. F. received two telephone calls from Mrs. Carver. The first had to do with her decision to retain an attorney: she wanted a divorce and needed Mr. F.'s help in finding an attorney. She couldn't say what had made her decide this about her marriage and the phone conversation became rather brief in response to Mr. F.'s suggestion that the discussion be put off until the following interview. About an hour later, she called again, saying that she wanted to do volunteer work and wanted us to provide her with some names and addresses of places that she could contact. She had decided against the divorce but wanted instead to get out of the house to do some kind of volunteer work or have a paying job. Mr. F. agreed to discuss these matters further in the interview.

In the individual interview with Mr. Carver, Mr. F. focused mainly on background information and tried to understand some of the precipitants of the current problems between the Carvers. He found that Mrs. Carver's natural parents had been divorced when she was about four years old. She had then made a series of moves, living with relatives in different cities. When Mr. Carver first met her, she was living with her mother in the same neighboring state. There were about three generations living in the household, including a grandfather, Mrs. Carver's mother, Mrs. Carver and several other relatives. Mrs. Carver and her mother then moved to Denver because Mrs. Russell thought that she could get a better job there.

Mr. Carver at first corresponded with his wife-to-be and eventually married her. The Carvers initially lived with Mrs. Russell in the latter's house. This living arrangement continued until about four years before, when Mrs. Russell remarried (for the second time). Apparently this depressed her daughter, since she had felt very tied to her. According to Mr. Carver, his wife talks nightly with her mother on the telephone and sees her mother in person about three times a week. In his very reserved and reluctant way, Mr. Carver admitted that his wife does not particularly care for *his* mother and that there is some tension when the two women are together. He thought that the recent trip to visit his mother may have contributed to the problems they were currently having.

Mr. Carver was very careful not to admit to any problems in his marriage. He felt that a change had taken place in his wife's personality after an automobile accident about four years before, which necessitated a hospital stay of six weeks. Apparently she had had some severe neck injuries, and he had the impression that since the accident his wife had been depressed and sometimes hard to get along with (the injury was subsequently confirmed but no psychic effects were recorded). According to Mr. Carver, his wife did not particularly enjoy her pregnancy with John and did not experience the normal elation over the first baby that Mr. Carver had seen in other women. However, he was quick to admit that she had done a fairly good job as a mother. Mr. Carver refused to believe that his wife had any serious ambitions to do any kind of work outside the home or have any contacts with other people. He felt that he had a very difficult job trying even to get her to visit friends.

In summary, Mr. Carver viewed his role with his wife as one in which he must constantly protect her and hover over her. It seemed during this interview that this view represented not only his own needs but also those of his wife for this kind of response from her husband. It seemed significant that her first psychiatric hospitalization, two years before, occurred when her mother and stepfather were off to visit the East coast: Mrs. Carver became very depressed and lonely. Mr. F. finally pointed out to Mr. Carver that his wife was expressing some interest in getting away from the house and wished not to have people protect her and guard her so carefully.

In Mr. F.'s interview he was careful not to endanger Mr. Carver's identity as the strong, providing male; in order to do this he did not question Mrs. Carver's need for help, care and protection. This tactic is somewhat unusual in that it preserves the role assignment made in the family; whenever possible and appropriate, FTU attempts to make a different definition of the current family situation, by pointing out to the family that all members are reacting to a common crisis, and that the symptoms of one are but one of the ways of reacting. Such a redefinition does not amount to a change in role assignments, which FTU's crisis treatment cannot aim for, but it does help the family question some of the assumptions it had made heretofore. In this case it was thought inadvisable to attempt such a redefinition; pointing out Mr. Carver's own dependent needs and defenses against them would have probably undermined his self esteem considerably and made it impossible to make him an ally in the few behavioral changes we were encouraging. In addition, the behavior requiring crisis treatment was but a worse form of that family's everyday behavior, and therefore too deeply rooted in the latter. It has been the experience of the FTU that long-term patterns are next to impossible to change in the context of crisis treatment and that in most cases they are better off left alone. With the Carvers they could not be left untouched altogether because of the way they intertwined with the current crisis and threatened to insure that similar ones would occur in the future as well; but they had nevertheless to be handled with extreme care, as Mr. F's interview illustrates.

The visit of the day before had been marked by our inability to persuade Mrs. Carver to talk about herself in any terms, not just affective but also factual. Mr. Carver had volunteered a lot of information as his wife was running in and out, but we had been unable to treat the two as a family. The distinction "patient—caring husband" had been preserved throughout. But after the interview it appeared to us that three issues were ones that we could bring up again and handle: Mrs. Carver's desire for independence from her husband in finding a job, her fears about bringing up her boy properly and without contradictory signals from her husband, and her desire not to be hovered over by the array of relatives that could be mobilized every time she showed signs of nervousness. On the third day, therefore, Dr. M. discussed these three issues with Mrs. Carver alone; he found her much calmer, more communicative, and above all, more informative. He discussed with her the sort of job she would like to take, what steps she had taken to obtain one, and what feelings she supposed her husband had about whether she would obtain employment or merely do volunteer work. He encouraged her efforts to find a job and gave her some relevant concrete advice. He assured her that she was a good mother to her son John and encouraged her to discuss with her husband whatever disagreements she might have about raising the child. Finally, he agreed with her desire that her mother-in-law and the mother-in-law's friend be encouraged to leave as soon as possible.

After a half-hour's individual interview with Mr. and Mrs. Carver, the therapists saw the two together. Mr. F. described the discussion he had had with Mr. Carver and Dr. M. described the one with his wife. Apparently the same issues that Dr. M. was encouraging Mrs. Carver to express herself on were the ones that Mr. F. was encouraging Mr. Carver to let Mrs. Carver make some decisions on. Thus their purposes were very much the same, and this brief final discussion seemed to go very well. Mrs. Carver asked her husband if they could not stop at the State Employment Bureau on their way from the offices to their house, and he agreed. It was expected (but not said) that he would of course continue to exercise control over their relationship, but there was on the one hand no hope of changing that long-term pattern, and on the other, no necessity for doing so as long as Mrs. Carver had her area of freedom and occasionally expressed her wants and desires.

This interview terminated our crisis intervention with the Carvers except for a request that they telephone us within two days to let us know how things were going.

Dr. M.'s portion of the individual interview also illustrates the degree to which FTU's endeavor was supportive. Mrs. Carver, now calm and self-possessed, seemed to be requesting some measure of freedom, and was asking her husband for permission and us for support; she was not actively rebelling against his authority. Even if she had not made such an appeal to us, we would have probably encouraged her search for outside employment, to the extent that we could make her husband accept it as best for her. What we were presented with was quite different from the more common situation: Mrs. Carver was asking to be *allowed* to function. For this reason our efforts were less directive and more supportive.

Nevertheless, the interview also makes clear that directiveness was as required in this case as it was in others; it was not applied to the question of functioning so much as to the manner in which Mrs. Carver might be allowed to function. It has been pointed out that we lacked a sense of the direction we should move in, and we remained uncomfortable until we found it between the second and third interviews; the discomfort came from the expectation we had formed of being able to direct the crisis toward resolution rather rapidly. With the Carvers the directness of our efforts had to do with persuading Mr. Carver of the reasonableness of what his wife was asking, and then helping her take concrete steps to achieve it.

Although we were persuaded of the desirability of Mrs. Carver's outside employment, and momentarily encouraged by the Carvers' response, we were doubtful of the degree of independence Mrs. Carver might successfully maintain. It is probably apparent from this discussion that Mr. Carver had a great deal at stake in his wife's dependence, but it can also be seen from Mr. F.'s interview that we saw Mrs. Carver as reassured by her husband's constant attention and unsure of her own competence (as seen in her self doubts as a mother). We thought it possible that today's move toward independence might be followed by tomorrow's toward childish dependence, and wondered what compromise between the two might be reached.

One further aspect of the last office visit should be stressed. We recapitulated for the Carvers our understanding of the crisis, and in so doing attempted to give them a measure of control over future ones. We pointed out to them that we did not know what had made Mrs. Carver edgy in the first place (although we had discovered that her son's return from preschool several months before had made some difference), but what had made matters especially bad was the manner in which her irritability was handled —by a well meant trip to relatives she did not get along with. We suggested therefore that since it was likely that Mrs. Carver would again become "nervous" sometime in the future, it would be best if she used a small dose of tranquilizer promptly; or, if she were not certain she wished to, that she or both of them should communicate with us quickly. We assured them that we continued to be available to them if they needed our help, and that in the future matters might very well be settled over the telephone, not requiring an office visit or longer treatment. We also told them that we would not ourselves be in touch with them except to send someone to their house in six months to conduct a follow-up visit.

Our next contact with them occurred as agreed, two days later and over the telephone; Dr. P. took the call.

Mr. Carver called to say that all was well with him and his wife. She was already at work, having obtained a job as a saleswoman. On Wednesday evening Mrs. Carver had gotten angry with her husband for being too attentive to his mother and ran away, later turning herself in to the police who brought her home. Mr. Carver responded by taking the unaccustomed role of being extremely firm and punitive. He threatened to leave her and take the child, told her that she was a terrible person to have done this and all of the other things she had done, and insisted that if he were to stay, she was going to have to be quite different. She tearfully agreed to all his conditions. Since that time she had obtained a job at which she was now working, had been doing all of the household chores that she had not done before, and in general, had been a model wife. Mr. Carver was quite pleased but perhaps a bit frightened by his new found power. He was advised to tell his wife to call Mr. F. on Monday.

As of two days after terminating treatment then, the outcome appeared to be a compromise between Mrs. Carver's contradictory wishes. On the one hand she was working outside the house and earning money on her own; on the other hand she had provoked her husband into taking a role more directly authoritative than usual, thus reassuring herself that she was an immature person in need of being watched over and directed in her more-or-less competent dealings with the world.

Several questions arise about the case, to which we should like to attempt answers. Several bits of information seem to be missing, partly about the Carvers' recent past (since their marriage), partly about their relation to significant people in the present, partly about ways in which we might have conducted treatment differently. For the present, however, it seems preferable to complete the chronological presentation and return to such questions subsequently. By including the information available to us over the six-month follow-up period, we shall at least answer questions relating to treatment outcome.

The next contact with the Carvers came in the form of a telephone call a month after the last. Mr. Carver was on the line and said that things had been going quite well. He thought that it had helped his wife to be working over the past five weeks. However, his wife was planning to stop working and could not give any specific reason except that she would like to spend more time around the house and with her son John. He had been attending a day nursery but since she would like to take John out of the nursery and take care of him full time once she stops working, Mr. Carver anticipated some difficulty. For his part, he would rather keep him in the nursery. We therefore anticipated further difficulty between the Carvers but noted with pleasure that Mr. Carver at least felt comfortable in calling us.

At this point after terminating treatment, Mrs. Carver seemed to have swung even further toward the dependency that she also needed to satisfy. She was on the point of giving up her job and wished to have her son at home with her, in spite of her knowledge that this had made her uncomfortable the last time and that she had complained it had been forced on her by circumstances. She seemed on the point of opening herself up to further irritation, of the kind she experienced a week or two before she had first come in contact with us. Nevertheless, matters never got out of the Carvers' control, and we had only one brief telephone call from them before the six-month follow-up. In this call Mrs. Carver wondered what had been the meaning of the form her husband had received and filled out without showing it to her. We explained that this was a routine form sent out three months after terminating treatment and that no one had intended that it be kept from her. She seemed calmed by the explanation and added that she would soon be going back to work. We did not ask for more information on how they were getting along, preferring not to stir up matters and wait until the follow-up visit.

Families are visited not only six months after terminating treatment but also at yearly intervals thereafter, for the duration of the research project. The follow-up consists of the administration of the same questionnaire forms as at intake, and of an interview, lasting an hour or two, conducted by a trained social worker. The aim of the interview is to gather information on how the family has been functioning since the last contact, what crises have been encountered (a prepared schedule is used for this purpose), how the family's economics stand, what the family's attitude is toward outpatient treatment as opposed to hospitalization, and any other impressions of a clinical nature that the case worker wishes to gather. The case worker is prepared ahead of time with certain information; he knows the family composition and reads a summary of the case prepared by the treatment team; in addition, he may be given a list of areas that should be particularly explored with the family he is about to see. The information gathered is then dictated and entered as part of the treatment record. As for the Carvers, we had asked the case worker to be particularly alert to information concerning Mrs. Carver's dependence-independence, the couple's relation to each other and to their extended family, and their young son's independence and his mother's handling of it.

Apropos of recent upsets, the interviewer reported that there had been two deaths in the family. Mrs. Carver's uncle died in June and her grandfather in July. She said she had been upset about her uncle's death but he was not as close as her grandfather, whose death had indeed been a problem. She thought that her grandfather's illness had contributed to the problems which had brought her to the hospital, since she had worried increasingly about it. After his death, however, she felt helped in a number of ways. She found, for example, that she was able to talk to her husband, a former mortician, about the death. But the most helpful person was her son, who kept saying on the way to the funeral, "Mother, don't get sick," and who therefore helped her not to worry too much. When she returned from the funeral, she had gone back to her job as salesgirl, and thought that the job was the needed "outlet" that had helped her after she terminated treatment with the FTU. She believed that an outlet was a much better answer to problems than visits to relatives. She particularly mentioned her mother-in-law, another worrier, who usually added to problems when there were already enough present. The job, she thought, helped because she was able to talk with her fellow employees. Her husband thought that his wife had handled the crisis quite well, and they did not request medication or further interviews.

It may be pointed out that Mrs. Carver's handling of the recent deaths illuminates her character in interesting ways. First, her grandfather's illness was apparently one of the stressors originally bringing her to the hospital doors, something she had not mentioned at all (although she also never took the opportunity to discuss *any* of the precipitants of her suicide gesture, preferring to remain mute in the first two interviews). Second, his death was experienced as a relief, presumably because he had been increasingly ill for some time. Third, the relief was all the stronger as she was able to transfer her dependence on her son, a boy of five. This in itself is striking, and seems to indicate not only that she felt less and less able to be closely dependent on her husband—a dependence she increasingly resented—but that the dependence was unusually strong and capable of resulting in a temporary reversal of generations; such a reversal is often noticed in the mothers of daughters in incestuous families, and although no similar pathology is implied here, it would be of concern to us were it to continue and deepen. Fourth, it should be remarked that Mrs. Carver had remembered FTU's interpretation of her feelings toward her in-laws, and gave free vent to it in the follow-up interview; she and her husband also remembered that we had suggested she take medication before problems got out of hand, but they had found a better remedy in her keeping busy outside the house.

The interviewer also noted that although Mrs. Carver felt that working had helped her, she had stopped in September when her son entered kindergarten at a local school. She said that the school requested that parents bring their children to school because of the dangerous street crossing, and she had quit her job in order to be able to do so. It may be noted, however, that when she had been working her husband had been able to take John to school. She added that at present she preferred to stay at home and work periodically as a substitute. When at home she could help her husband with his filing and phone calls, since his home is his office. Her one other activity was the church, but most of her time seemed to be bound up in the home. Her husband said that he thought his wife was better away from home and she seemed to agree—but they both seemed comfortable with the present arrangement. The fact that Mrs. Carver knows there is an "out" is probably sufficient, but apparently she prefers to be at home. Her husband may say that his wife is better out of the home, but he finds her helpful in his business.

Mrs. Carver also mentioned that her son's having entered kindergarten probably indicates that he needs her less. At the end of the hour she said, "See, I didn't have to check on John while he was playing outside." She did raise the question, "How will I react as John takes further steps toward independence?" Finally she said she hoped she could be different from her mother-in-law, who had difficulty letting her own son go.

Although Mr. Carver claimed that his wife needed more "outlets," it was clear that his choices were not necessarily those of his wife. He was more concerned with the P.T.A. and club activities, while she seemed to prefer church work and her job as saleslady. Although Mrs. Carver initially seemed rather quiet, she became more communicative during the hour. Earlier, instead of voicing her own opinion, she would let her husband speak for her, and then resentfully retreat into silence. By the end of the hour she was able to differ with him around her own interests and to indicate difficulties connected with having her husband's business in the house.

In the interviewer's summary, Mrs. Carver's compromise between dependence and independence seemed to have been accomplished rather stably. Her dependent feelings seemed stronger and more constant than her desires for independence, and the latter appeared to become strong only after a period of excessive withdrawal to her home or in response to other stresses; for this reason, the currently satisfactory outcome was to stay primarily home but always to have the possibility of getting out for awhile. One might speculate that the husband's need to protect fitted only too well her desire to be protected; it occasionally reached a point of satiation (with her) and needed disruption, if only temporarily.

In some respects the family had reached a somewhat higher level of functioning than before the crisis that had brought them to our attention. Mrs. Carver was able to anticipate certain stresses ahead of time and reach thereby at least partial solutions in fantasy; such was her speculation about her son's further steps toward independence, and her pride at allowing him more than she feared she might be able to. And the couple were able to tolerate levels of disagreement that seemed unimaginable previously; Mrs. Carver could express disagreement, and her husband could live with it.

One might well ask whether the Carvers, in view of their previously shown desire to please, were not attempting to put themselves in a favorable light by appearing to have reached levels of functioning which we had held up to them as desirable. Such a possibility cannot altogether be dismissed, but seems only a partial explanation of the changes observable in the interview; in addition to those, there is the unmistakable fact of the Carvers' ability to handle crises without resort to hospitalization, or even to medications or calls to the FTU. In that sense, the aim of therapy seems to have been successful, and in Mrs. Carver's ability to disagree, to leave the house occasionally, and to allow her son to grow up, is reflected a better level of functioning than we had expected.

In view of the Carvers' equilibrium at the time of the follow-up, it is difficult to look back over the therapeutic attempts critically and propose inadequacies in the manner in which the case was handled. Nevertheless, certain questions about the case require further speculation. We were both surprised by the time of the third interview that we had not wished to see more of Mrs. Russell; the relation between her and her daughter was so close as to invite further examination. In retrospect, we believe that we were persuaded that the relation, though not conforming to our desires, was nevertheless stable and unproblematic; both mother and daughter enjoyed it, and so did Mr. Carver, who apparently was fond of his mother-in-law. Subsequent events seem to indicate, so far, that the relation continues to be without major difficulties, and perhaps justify what was at that time only an unconscious decision on our part. Less satisfactory is our omission from the therapeutic interviews of Mr. Carver's mother and her friend, who had both brought Mrs. Carver from their home to our hospital doors. Although there was some resistance on everyone's part against their participation (at the second interview they were asleep and the Carvers were content to let them remain so), somewhat greater pressure on our part would have brought them out of their momentary retreat. In general, when the FTU attempts to encourage an individual's independence, the one he should be independent from has to be partner to the negotiations. In this case, the outcome seems to indicate that Mrs. Carver was able quite on her own to admit, express, and act on her desire to be more distant from her in-laws, but the change came about in spite of what we believe is usually more effective, interpersonal procedure. Quite far from indicating our efficacy in producing lasting changes with short-term treatment, the change occurred over and above our efforts and expectations.

Finally, it does not seem inappropriate to mention the Carvers' feelings about the relative merits of hospitalization and outpatient treatment for their case, because they seem to us to indicate some of the advantages of an interpersonal approach to the treatment of crises arising out of longstanding marital patterns—as well as indicating that we had not perhaps pursued those advantages as far as might have been possible.

In response to the interviewer's question, both Mrs. and Mr. Carver said that they preferred being treated in the Family Treatment Unit. In fact, they seemed startled when it was suggested that hospitalization would have been the alternative. Mr. Carver said that he thought the treatment had been too brief; he would have liked a little more "orientation and counseling," because it was very easy to become "impatient" with his wife. She said that she felt helped by her husband's increased attention and said that they took long walks together and talked about her feelings.

CHAPTER 8

Evaluating Family Crisis Therapy

This chapter is about evaluating families generally and evaluating family crisis therapy specifically. The field of family psychology is a very new one and a much younger discipline than the psychology of the individual. There are vast numbers of tests which have been developed to evaluate individual patients. Only a few psychologic tests for entire families have been worked out. Even this brief review of the instruments used to measure families by other investigators seems useful because it highlights the special testing requirements of the Family Treatment Unit. We will initially review the approaches to testing in family research and will then describe the research design to test the comparative effectiveness of family crisis therapy and mental hospital treatment.

"MEASURING" FAMILIES

There have been two general approaches to developing instruments for measuring families. One type is a diagnostic approach. This approach aims to develop diagnostic methods for single families. The investigator has usually chosen to put his energies into complex and time-consuming description of a few families. The other general category attempts to answer questions about families in general. This approach usually favors a large sample of families. The complexity of family phenomena may be minimized in order to use a larger sample. The classification of these two approaches is not an either-or phenomenon. Nonetheless, in actual practice one can divide the family tests which have been developed into those diagnostic procedures given to a small number of cases and aiming for relatively complete description, and those less complex instruments given to much larger numbers of families and which tap more descriptive or "superficial" phenomena.

This latter, large sample approach might be termed "hypothesis research." Hypothesis research generally uses simpler technics. It is often a research approach in which there is an attempt to test for differences between two groups of families such as pathologic versus normal. At other times the technics simply aim to gather normative data on a single population without attempting to contrast it with some other group. The interaction testing of Bauman and Roman[1] looks at the differences between individual and common performance on intelligence tests given to married couples. The aim of this testing is to find factors that influence marital dominance. The coalitions game of Haley[5] contrasts coalition patterns in normal and schizophrenic families. Haley's relatively unstructured situation[6] looks for patterns of speech sequences among three family members. Both of the Haley tests attempt to discover differences between normal and abnormal families. The family TAT story task developed by Ferreira, Winter and Poindexter,[3] like the Haley methods, searches for normal-abnormal differences. The variables of this family TAT are the speech lengths of family members. One of its more ambitious goals is to attempt to distinguish different types within the pathologic group. The Parental Attitude Research Instrument, described by Zuckerman et al.,[14] measures mothers' attitudes toward children and child rearing by means of a questionnaire. Its aim is to provide normative data on the relationship of child-rearing attitudes to certain demographic variables. Hypothesis research thus aims to discover relations between at least two variables, a purpose which the diagnostic testing generally ignores.

In considering methods to evaluate the results of family crisis therapy, we have been influenced by certain considerations. The first consideration is that it seems easier to detect differences between groups of families than to measure changes in one family over time. A cross sectional comparison of two sets of families would be more likely to show differences between the groups than a longitudinal approach. Family patterns, especially those which have been going on for a long time, do not change easily. Furthermore, longitudinal studies which show changes over a long period of time are subject to another criticism. If one finds changes occurring over many years and tries to relate these changes to a single independent variable, then the investigator is likely to be asked about the effect of all of the many things that have happened to the family during that lengthy time period. Thus for this type of clinical research, a cross sectional comparison of two groups has advantages over longitudinal studies within a single family. Another factor which has influenced our attempts to measure the results of family therapy is the difficulty of obtaining "before-after" differences in families. Haley[6] has shown that family patterns do not change even after considerable treatment. It would, therefore, be unrealistic to expect that brief therapy for families would result in measurable interactional differences applied on a before-after basis. For this reason, our attention has been focused on measuring before-after differences in *individuals*. We shall, however, describe one attempt at devising a family measure which might prove of diagnostic use.

Diagnostic research aims for a complex description of a small number of families. The emphasis is on understanding each family as an entity. One example of such a diagnostic test is the Color Matching test of Goodrich and Boomer.[4] In this test married couples are asked to resolve artifically produced disagreements. The aim of the technic is to describe modes of conflict resolution in the marital pair. In the Communicator-Communicant approach, Levin[7] uses individuals who send verbal descriptions of a geometric figure to a specific "other" person. This other person is represented by a tape recorder. This research looks for normal-abnormal differences, but it resembles diagnostic studies since the variables are not always clearly defined and depend on broad clinical judgments. The Family Rorschach was developed independently by Loveland, Wynne, and Singer[9] and by Levy and Epstein.[8] It requires family members to attempt to reach a common interpretation of a Rorschach blot previously described individually. The areas explored by the Family Rorschach include methods of conflict resolution, other areas of family difficulties, and the interrelations between individual and family psychopathology. The Family Relations Test, developed by Bene and Anthony and described by Meyer[11] is oriented towards the child's perception of other members of his family. In this test the child is asked to describe members of his family by matching descriptive statements with figures drawn to represent the family members. This description by the child is complex but is presumably valid as one picture of the family as a group. Terrill and Terrill[13] have adapted the Leary Interpersonal Circle to families. They analyze the verbal utterances of family members on the intersecting dimensions of dominance-submission and hostility-affiliation. A technic such as the Revealed Differences of Strodtbeck[12] seems useful in confronting family members with their disagreements and asking them for a resolution. The resulting interaction is rich in possibilities for diagnostic analysis.

Despite the proposed distinction between hypothesis research and diagnostic research, we would like to describe an instrument which has been used in both ways. It has seemed most suited for measuring certain stable family patterns. In developing this test, there seemed little possibility of using it to measure family change. Theoretically we have been convinced that crisis family therapy may resolve a crisis but does not achieve change in long term family interactional patterns. Therefore, the emphasis in the use of the Family Task Inventory (as we call this test) has been to find diagnostic information about a single family which would distinguish it from other families. In addition, we have hoped to use the FTI to make comparisons of certain groups of families with other groups.

The FTI is a paper-and-pencil measure designed to assess family task distribution. It was developed by Dr. Andrew Ferber of Albert Einstein College of Medicine and modified slightly by the psychologist of the Family Treatment Unit (P.M.).[10] This instrument asks each family member to describe every other member of the family on the frequency with which he performs each of a large number of tasks required for the family's daily life. By constructing an index of each member's importance (in task performance), as seen by himself and others, and by looking at the discrepancies among these indices, one can obtain an interesting diagnostic picture of families. This has been found to correlate with clinical judgment. The picture of the family includes, for example, indices of the task-performing importance of the father and mother. It may show the manner in which certain members under or over-value them. It includes the family's view of its communication pattern with a distribution of who talks to whom, under what circumstances, and how often. Judgments made from these indices imply covert or explicit comparisons with other families. This has been the diagnostic research related to the use of this instrument. The hypothesis research with the FTI consists of a cluster analysis of the items. The cluster analysis seeks to find what tasks make up specific roles within the family. The results of our initial analyses

as reported by Machotka and Ferber[10] indicate that while it is often
thought that the paternal role is predominantly "instrumental" and
the maternal, mostly "expressive," the number of instrumental tasks
which fathers perform is small compared to those performed by
mothers.

The review of work done by others in the field and the experience
gained measuring some patterns with the FTI have had a strong
influence on our own evaluative efforts. They have helped us to
decide to measure change in individuals rather than focusing exclusively on change within families. They have helped us to concentrate on the social adjustment and symptoms of the individual
within the family rather than on long-term interpersonal patterns.

EVALUATION RESEARCH

The aim of family crisis therapy is to help families which include
one member who has decompensated sufficiently to request admission to a mental hospital. The primary aim of the treatment is recompensation. This is attempted by the technics which are outlined
in Chapter 2 and throughout the rest of this book. We focus most
often on the sequence of events which led to a request for hospitalization. Additionally, the crisis team encourages the patient
and other family members to return to functioning at the pre-crisis
level. Since the goal of treatment is a return to functioning and a
remission of the symptoms of decompensation, the evaluation of
treatment focuses on the way in which the identified patient performs his role in the family and the symptomatology of illness and
dysfunction. The results of any psychiatric treatment could focus
on the outcome of the treatment itself but there is no single criterion
measure that satisfies all investigators. Freud suggested that the
measure of the outcome of psychoanalytic therapy was a test of
whether the patient could work and love. Although these may seem
like simple criteria, they do focus on behavior. These criteria may
imply change in personality structure, the quality and type of object relationships, and the absence of pathologic defenses, but they
are descriptions of behavioral results.

Other investigators have used a variety of measures. Changes in
the symptoms or the manifestations of illness are a classical approach. The clinician studying a treatment for an infectious disease

which causes fever would certainly follow the temperature of his patients. Others compare the results of a treatment by focusing on the description of the treatment itself. The length of hospital stay and subsequent rehospitalization of the patients studied have been chosen as one way to measure the effectiveness of a treatment. Others study personality structure as a criterion for the assessment of the results of treatment. For the most part, these have been measures of the results of outpatient psychotherapy. The pragmatist will generally focus on how well the patient is adapting to his own environment. In view of the fact that a large proportion of the population has been adjudged to be "psychiatrically ill" by various epidemiologic studies, it would seem well to focus on whether or not the patient is getting along in his own social milieu. Though we know there are many schizophrenics in the community, it does make a difference as to whether or not they are supporting themselves, fulfilling their role functions within their families or whether they are independent and crippled as chronic patients in a mental hospital.

We have chosen to compare the results of family crisis therapy and mental hospital treatment using a variety of criteria. However, it was first necessary to be sure that the two groups treated were comparable. The basic design in carrying on the evaluation called for a random selection of cases from a population of patients who were about to be admitted to Colorado Psychiatric Hospital. In order to be eligible for possible random selection, the patients had to have presented themselves in the emergency room and after evaluation, the psychiatric resident decided that the patient needed to be admitted *immediately* to the Psychiatric Hospital. The patients who required immediate admission to the hospital and who lived with a relative between sixteen and sixty years of age and who lived within an hour's travel from Colorado Psychiatric Hospital, constituted the population from which the sample was drawn. The only additional requirement was that the patients were voluntary admissions. The psychiatric resident who decided to admit the patient to the hospital who met these criteria would telephone the Family Treatment Unit before arranging for admission. A previously prepared sealed envelope was opened by the FTU team member on call and only then would the FTU or the psychiatric resident in the emergency room learn whether the patient was to be admitted or to be assigned to the Family Treatment Unit. Those rejected by this random procedure became a pool of potential control cases. They would be admitted to the hospital immediately, would receive regular hospital treatment, but would be tested by the Family Treatment Unit in the same manner as the family crisis therapy cases were tested. The controls as a group have been matched with the experimental cases. No other process of selection operates. All evaluative results, therefore, are in the forms of comparison between the experimental and control cases (family crisis treatment and hospital treatment cases). All cases are tested at intake, six months after discharge, and at yearly intervals thereafter for the duration of the project. Each family receives at least two follow-ups. Some can be followed for as many as five years.

The evaluation consists of comparisons between the experimental and control group on a number of basic criteria:

(1) *Subsequent mental hospital admissions.* Crisis family therapy is aimed not only at finding an alternative to hospitalization during the treatment itself. It also hopes to help the family work out other methods of crisis resolution in the future. If this aim is accomplished, there should be a lower subsequent hospitalization rate among the experimental (family crisis therapy) cases than among the hospitalized controls. If family crisis treatment has only been able to provide an alternative to hospitalization at the time of the acute illness, the rates of rehospitalization should be the same.

(2) *Social Adjustment Inventory Scores.* The Social Adjustment Inventory, developed by Berger et al.[2] measures the adaptation of the patient on four subscales and assigns a total score of adjustment. The subscales include social and family relations, social productivity, self-management, and anti-social behavior. The questionnaire obtains information about the patient's marital status, employment, self-management, social contacts, etc. It is answered for the patient by a member of his family and by a friend. The baseline scores are compared with postdischarge scores as rated by the same person. Change scores for the experimental cases are compared with change scores for the control cases.

(3) *Personal Functioning Scale.* The Personal Functioning Scale is a questionnaire developed by the Family Treatment Unit which is intended to probe some of the areas which are also measured in the Social Adjustment Inventory. Thus, it is an instrument

which should provide a measure of reliability. However, it also measures symptoms of mental illness, an area not tapped by the SAI. Scores on the PFS measure the adequacy of functioning of the identified patient in work, household or school tasks. The performance of the housewife belongs to the second category and the student to the third. In addition, there are questions about the symptoms of psychopathology and the degree to which the physical health of the patient interferes with his functioning. This scale is administered to the identified patient and to one member of his family. Change scores are computed for each rater and then compared between the experimental and control groups.

(4) *Clinical Evaluation of Family Functioning.* Professional psychiatric social workers who have no other connection with the project interview each family at the time of the postdischarge testing. They gather information on the family according to an interview schedule made out by the Family Treatment Unit. Of particular interest in these clinical ratings are the family's overall economic situation, the family's ways of handling crises that have arisen since the last testing, changes in family composition, and the rater's overall evaluation and impression of the family's functioning and cohesion. Such variables may not be able to be expressed in simple numerical scores. They are expected, however, to add "flesh" to the skeleton of the scores calculated by the methods above. They offer a clinical approach to the differences between the experimental and control groups.

(5) *Post-treatment Crises and Their Management.* At each follow-up the family completes a checklist of hazardous events which may have been encountered since the last contact with the Family Treatment Unit. A detailed description of each stressor is recorded as is the manner in which the family handled it. The hazardous events and the management of each event is scored according to whether the family managed the problem on its own or sought help from an outside agency or went to a mental hospital. Families which encounter many hazardous events or especially severe ones are expected to show poorer functioning than families which encounter few. In addition, the experimental and control samples may be found to differ in the self-sufficiency with which they handle crises.

Other studies have been undertaken which will look at the process of the evaluation itself and attempt to find predictors of treatment success. One scale called the "Family Profile" is completed by the clinical treatment team. It consists of variables that are thought to predict treatment success in families seen by the Family Treatment Unit. The presumed predictors are mostly clinical (such as whether the family was cooperative in carrying out assigned tasks, whether the extended family was involved in the crisis, etc.). Treatment success is defined by the functioning of the patient and the family before and after the presenting crisis. Simple and partial correlations between predictors and outcome are the basic data which this study attempts to uncover.

Another study attempts to discover nonclinical correlates of success. These include family composition, number of previous hospitalizations, social class, and other data. These data are taken from a special family outline which serves the purpose of recording data about the families treated and of forming a permanent record of cases treated. It is coded and arranged in such a manner that the data are placed on IBM punch cards and therefore the information is readily retrievable.

A third additional study consists of a group of subprojects. These include many tangential but clinically interesting issues which are not part of the basic design of the comparison of treatment results. However, any clinical research project will stimulate subsidiary questions. Some of these can be tested without altering the basic series of measurements and therefore have been carried out. Since they are not part of the basic research design, they will be described elsewhere.

SUMMARY

In this chapter we have attempted to list the established psychologic instruments used to "measure" families and we have also reviewed the basic evaluation research design together with the tests used in that study.

Bibliography

1. Bauman, Gerald and Roman, Melvin. Interaction testing in the study of marital dominance. Family Process. 5:230-42, 1966.

2. Berger, David G., Rice, Charles E., Sewall, Lee G., and Lemkau, Paul V. Post-hospital evaluation of psychiatric patients: the social adjustment inventory method. A.P.A. Psychiatric Studies and Projects. #15, 1964.

3. Ferreira, A. H., Winter, W. D. and Poindexter, E. J. Some interactional variables in normal and abnormal families. Family Process 5:60–75, 1966.

4. Goodrich, D. W. and Boomer, D. S. Experimental assessment of modes of conflict resolution. Family Process. 2:15-24, 1963.

5. Haley, Jay. Family experiments: a new type of experimentation. Family Process. 1:265-93, 1962.

6. Haley, Jay. Research on family patterns: an instrument measurement. Family Process. 3:41-65, 1964.

7. Levin, G. Communicator-communicant approach to family interaction research. Family Process. 5:105-16, 1966.

8. Levy, J. and Epstein, N. B. An application of the Rorschach test in family investigation. Family Process. 3:344-76, 1964.

9. Loveland, Nathene T., Wynne, Lyman C. and Singer, Margaret T. The family Rorschach: a new method for studying family interaction. Family Process. 2:187-215, 1963.

10. Machotka, P. and Ferber, A. S. Delineation of family roles. Presented at American Orthopsychiatric Association, April 1967.

11. Meyer, M. M. Family relations test. J. Project. Techn. 27:309-14, 1963.

12. Strodtbeck, F. L. Family interaction, values, and achievement. In: McClelland, D. C. et al. Talent and Society. Princeton: Van Nostrand, 1958.

13. Terrill, J. M. and Terrill, Ruth E. A method for studying family communication. Family Process. 4:259-90, 1965.

14. Zuckerman, M., Ribback, B. B., Monashkin, I. and Norton, J. A. Jr. Normative data and factor analysis on the Parental Attitude Research Instrument. J. Consult. Psychol. 22:165-71, 1958.

CHAPTER 9

The Results of Family Crisis Therapy

What happens when patients who would have been hospitalized receive family crisis therapy instead? At this time we can offer a clinical description. Follow-up data is being gathered which will permit a systematic comparison of the effects of family crisis therapy and mental hospital treatment. It would be tempting but premature to report the encouraging preliminary results. We will report, however, the comparison of the first 75 experimentals and controls in regard to subsequent mental hospitalization within six months of termination. This comparison should answer the question of whether this brief outpatient approach really avoids or merely postpones mental hospitalization. We do wish to make it clear, however, that we are gathering extensive follow-up data on the 150 experimental cases, the 150 control cases, and the 36 pilot cases, and will have a minimum of six and eighteen month follow-ups on all cases.

The random assignment of cases from the same population to the experimental group (family crisis therapy) or the controls (mental hospitalization) gives us some confidence that the groups are comparable. This similarity of the two groups that are being compared is, of course, essential. Unless they were similar groups we would be comparing the effects of different treatments on different populations. The preliminary comparisons of the two groups (75 experimentals and 75 controls) show that there are no differences on 15 of 15 categories. The 15 variables include data about the patient, type of family, the admission diagnosis, history of previous mental hospitalization, age, etc.

In reviewing here the effects of family crisis therapy, we will look at three areas—the community, the family, and the individual patient. The results of family crisis therapy on the individual patient's state of crisis, functioning and clinical symptoms will be explored. In addition, the subsequent history of the individual patient should be examined. Assuming that he gets over the crisis, what happens to him later? Does the crisis repeat itself immediately? Does he learn to handle crises in a new way or does the patient get hospitalized with the next crisis? Are we really preventing hospitalization or do we merely delay it? The effects of family crisis therapy on the family itself must be examined. What happens to the family of the identified patient? If we do keep the patient out of the mental hospital, what does this do to the family? Again the immediate effects and the follow-up result should be examined. In addition to the individual and family, the effects on the community should be examined. What happens to the community when one keeps psychiatric patients out of mental hospitals and permits them to remain in their usual jobs and homes?

THE INDIVIDUAL—THE IDENTIFIED PATIENT

The first effects of crisis therapy are a lessening of tension in the patient. The tension and pressure which are the hallmarks of a state of crisis are reduced by the rest, the expectation of help and by whatever medication may have been used initially. In the Simpson case (Chapter 4) the husband came into the emergency room obviously very fearful that he was about to lose control. He was afraid of "cracking up," was depressed, had lost twenty pounds and was having trouble sleeping. His subjective emotional state and the objective evidence of his behavior indicated the heightened state of tension and pressure from which he suffered. Within twenty-four hours this tension and pressure were diminished simply because he was reassured by the expectation that the experts would help him and by the reassurance and suggestions that he would not lose control. In addition, a night's rest had set in motion his own recuperative powers. In the case of Mrs. Carver (Chapter 7) the most intense pressure had been experienced during the visit to her in-laws in Kansas when she made a suicide attempt. By the time she was seen by the Treatment Unit, she had already exhibited signs of lessening of the tension. In her case the tension diminished when her husband brought her back to her own home in Colorado and then to the psychiatric admitting service. But here, too, the combination of a promise of help and rest brought rapid lessening of the internal pressure.

The consequence of lowering the tension level (in the patient or in the family) is that the individual frees up the problem-solving capacities which were formerly paralyzed by his crisis condition. It has been repetitively shown that people in crisis do not function efficiently. In a natural disaster such as earthquake, flood or tornado, the people affected initially experience a state of shock. They are paralyzed and helpless during the acute response. The same thing is true of a person in crisis. Once his state of shock or paralyses is diminished by the relationship with the helpers, by medication and by rest, he begins to view his problem with new perspective. As Mr. Simpson became less tense and upset, he was able to participate with the team in arranging for a meeting with his wife. In the case of Portia Jones (Chapter 5), she became more communicative and more able to use logical reason rather than the primitive psychotic mechanisms employed during the crisis. Continued work with Portia and her family permitted the treatment team to make contact with her on the problem of getting a job. These coping technics or problem-solving capacity are essential to normal function. A crisis state paralyzes them as effectively as a broken leg inhibits walking. The relaxation of tension permits their return.

Psychoanalytic ego psychology would suggest that neutralized ego energies are seriously diminished by the emergency state of a crisis. The crisis requires all available energies to insure the intactness of the individual's ego. The lessening of tension has the economic effect of making available neutralized energy and previously successful coping mechanisms.

The clinical symptoms should now begin to disappear. The symptoms of the clinical syndrome or the mental illness is not subject to simplistic explanation. Why one patient becomes depressed as a result of tension or crisis and another exhibits delusional thinking while yet another loses control of his behavior, is a complex phenomenon. It will depend upon the past history of the individual and his lifelong patterns of solving problems. It will depend upon the family setting and other factors in his social milieu. It will depend upon his inherited constitution and his present physiologic state. But *the object of crisis therapy is not to explain and understand symptoms. It is to improve the current situation so as to diminish the need for regressive and pathologic behavior, affects and thinking.* Portia Jones demonstrated catatonic symptoms, psychotic thought processes, and the highly primitive communication patterns of an acute schizophrenic reaction. Within the first interview she began to respond to the treatment team as help was offered. Her psychotic state did not clear immediately. During the evening of the first contact she continued to show highly regressive behavior including the primitive physical contact needs which were misinterpreted by her parents as a wish for adult sexual experiences. By the next afternoon, after rest and medication, Portia was out of bed and talking more coherently to her father. Again that evening (thirty hours after the team's first contact) Portia responded to a religious healing service with a repetition of her regressive behavior. But by the eighth day Portia was able to be out of the home visiting a friend. On the ninth day, during a family treatment session, she was "vivacious, attractive, charming and flirtatious."

Similarly, Mr. Simpson's symptoms cleared rapidly. Within five days (the joint interview with his wife took place on the third day) his depression had lifted and he was describing in more realistic terms, the possibility of a divorce. He was discussing with the team what might be the eventual outcome if there were a legal separation. Mr. Simpson's symptoms of intense fear over loss of control, and his angry ruminations over the role of the neighbor in his marital problems were no longer of serious concern. In the Carver case the wife was no longer depressed and suicidal. Her symptoms abated within the first day or two.

To recapitulate, the immediate effects of crisis treatment for the individual patient include lessening of tension, remission of symptoms, and a freeing up of problem solving potential so that more adaptive coping devices can be used. A *recompensation* is taking place. A suicide or homicide may be prevented. The patient and other people around him are protected from the primitive rages and destructive states associated with a regressive psychotic illness. The evidence that there has been a return to function is visible immediately. The patient can return to work or return to school or return to household duties very rapidly. Within a few days Mr. Simpson had found a job as a janitor. Whereas he had been living with his sister and brother-in-law because of the emergency, he became able to find a furnished room near his new job and establish his own living quarters. Portia Jones showed remarkable and dramatic behavioral changes within a week and within two weeks was making plans with the treatment team to find a job. These behavioral alterations are evidence of change in the crisis situation. They are not evidence of change in long-term patterns of adaptation or alteration of chronic problems. Because crisis treatment produces rapid and dramatic changes in behavior and in symptom, it is tempting to assume that it is the treatment for all types of emotional problems. Crisis therapy is effective for crises! It does not produce the same kind of result when the problem is a long-term or chronic situation. Physicians have long known that acute illness is improved by nonspecific support. If there is a specific treatment such as penicillin for the pneumococcus, so much the better! Chronic illness does not show the immediate or rapid changes expected in the treatment of an acute problem.

The clinical changes noted above are the immediate results and the most visible manifestations. Another change which is hoped for is that the patient learns new ways of dealing with subsequent crises. There will, of course, be subsequent crises! One of the surest things about life is the fact that it is problematic. Time will bring other crises. These, too, will be accompanied by increased tension which, if continued, may result in regression and the symptoms of mental illness. To help a patient out of one trap is no guarantee that he won't fall into another. However, those who do crisis therapy hope that patients will learn how to deal more efficiently with future crises. The treatment team tries to teach the patient and the family that help is available. Having had the experience of successful resolution of one crisis, the patient and family may return to that source of help for future troubles. By the time any of these cases reached the Family Treatment Unit, the patient and family or other helper have decided that a mental hospitalization is necessary. Clinical experience has taught us that when the mental hospital is seen as the way to solve problems, it will be used again for future problems. The classic example of the use (or misuse) of the psychiatric hospital as a problem solving resource is the alcoholic patient. In some states alcoholism is treated by committing the patient permanently (or in some cases for several years) to a state mental hospital. When he arrives at the hospital, he is "dried out," given vitamins and other nonspecific therapy, and within a month or two is placed on "temporary discharge" or on "convalescent leave." This legal status means that the patient can be returned to the hospital with a minimum of administrative procedure. Generally a phone call and the verbal authorization of any staff member of the state mental hospital is adequate. The patient has been "permanently committed." In this situation the family call on the mental hospital when the patient drinks. Since he is labeled "alcoholic" and since the hospital has been made the solution to the problems created by his drinking, he is sent back to the hospital each time he gets drunk. On the other hand, the hospital has no magical cure for alcoholism. Hospitalization doesn't really change the drinking problem; it only houses the patient, dries him out. It may be a temporary solution to the immediate difficulties of the family or the community, but as has been pointed out in the introduction, it is an expensive, inefficient treatment.

On the other hand, if the family and the community as well as the patient, learn that crisis resolution can be accomplished without hospitalization, a new approach to problem solving may be the result. If this is to be successful, the same conditions must apply to the subsequent crisis treatment as apply to the original crisis therapy. The help must be immediately forthcoming. A crisis, by definition, requires immediate action. Clinic waiting lists have not proved to be good treatment for crises.

But have the Family Treatment Unit's services proved useful for later crises? The use of the hospital for the management of subsequent crises has been examined in 75 cases treated by admission to Colorado Psychiatric Hospital and in 75 cases treated by family crisis therapy. As was stated in the beginning of this chapter, the two groups have been shown to be comparable.

Of the 75 family crisis treatment cases, *none* were hospitalized during the crisis treatment. Instead of being hospitalized they were treated by an average of 4.2 office sessions, 1.6 home visits, 4.5 telephone calls and 1.3 contacts with other social agencies. This treatment took place over an average of 22.7 days. Of the 75 control cases, all were hospitalized. They were in the hospital a total of 1,959 days, or an average of 26.1 days per case. In other words, none of the experimentals and 100 per cent of the controls became mental hospital patients as a result of the current problem and the treatment approach.

What about subsequent hospitalization? The 75 cases in each group are shown in Table 1. Those cases labeled "FTU" are the Family Treatment Unit or the experimental cases. The controls are the cases admitted to Colorado Psychiatric Hospital. It will be seen that there are very significant differences between the two groups during the six months after treatment. For the controls (hospital cases) 13 or 17 per cent of the sample are rehospitalized within a month after discharge. Over the next five months an additional three of the 75 cases were readmitted to a psychiatric hospital. By the end of six months, 21 per cent of the sample had been readmitted to a mental hospital. Of the 75 FTU cases, only five were admitted to a mental hospital during the first month. This represents 7 per cent of the sample rather than 17 per cent. By the end of six months, a total of 14 patients had been hospitalized at one point or the other. This does not look enormously different for experimentals and controls. It would suggest that perhaps we have only delayed hospitalization rather than prevented it. If we had only delayed hospitalization, our subsequent hospitalization rate would be much higher than that of the controls. In fact it is *lower*. This six month follow-up shows that 83 per cent of the experimentals have *never* been admitted to the mental hospital (after initial contact with the FTU). Of the controls, on the other hand, 100 per cent were admitted to a mental hospital initially and an additional 21 per cent are readmitted during the first six months after treatment. This is the real difference between the two groups.

Are there other differences? If comparable numbers of cases in the experimental and the control groups are hospitalized during the first six months *after* treatment, have we taught the FTU cases anything new about crisis management? Have we taught them how to deal with crises without admission to a mental hospital? In order to try to answer this question we have examined the number of potential hospital days actually spent in a mental hospital by the experimentals and the controls. This is done by assuming that each month has thirty days, and that if all patients were in a mental hospital all the time during that particular month, the percentage of potential hospital days actually utilized would be 100 per cent. If no patient was ever hospitalized during that month, the figure shown in the column would be 0 per cent. An examination of the data for experimentals and controls (in Table 1) shows that the

Table 1

Rehospitalization of 75 Family Crisis Therapy Cases and 75 Hospital Cases (Controls)

	Cumulative # of patients hospitalized		Cumulative # of hospital days		Cumulative # of potential hospital days	% of potential hospital days used this month		% of sample not hospitalized	
	FTU	Control	FTU	Control		FTU	Control	FTU	Control
Acute treatment period	None	75	None	1,959		None	100%	100%	83%
1st post-treatment month	5	13	69	211	2,250	3.1%	9.4%	93%	83
2nd month	8	13	151	401	4,500	3.6	8.4	89	81
3rd month	10	14	242	554	6,750	4.0	6.8	87	79
4th month	11	16	307	753	9,000	2.9	8.8	85	79
5th month	13	16	365	933	11,250	2.6	8.0	83	79
6th month	14	16	423	1,091	13,500	2.6	7.0	81	79
Average						3.1	8.1		

control cases (those treated by admission to a mental hospital) spend about three times as many days in a hospital as do the experimental cases. The figures for the experimental cases are on the order of three per cent of potential hospital days actually spent in the hospital during any given month. On the other hand, the controls show about three times as many potential hospital days actually occupied. The percentage is constant throughout the six months ranging from eight to ten per cent. Another way of looking at this data is to note the accumulated number of hospital days actually spent in the hospital for each group during the total six months. Table 1 shows that this number is 423 for the experimental group and 1,091 for the control group. We cannot say that the number of patients who are actually admitted to a mental hospital during the six months after treatment are grossly different for the experimentals or the controls, but the amount of time spent in a mental hospital is very different. Of the 75 experimental cases only 14 were ever hospitalized either during the acute treatment phase or during the ensuing six months. Of the 75 control cases, all 75 were admitted to a mental hospital for treatment and during the next six months 16 of the 75 were *again* admitted to a psychiatric hospital.

There is another effect of not admitting a patient to a mental hospital during the treatment of a crisis. By not admitting him, we avoid labeling the patient as "crazy" or as a "mental patient." Of the 75 FTU cases referred to above, 62 were never hospitalized during the acute illness or during the ensuing six months. What does this mean to the individual patient? Among other things it means that the patient will have far less trouble getting his driver's license renewed or getting a job or getting insurance. In the state of Colorado (as in many other states) a person is asked whether he has been in a mental hospital when he gets his driver's license. If he answers affirmatively, he is required to obtain a medical report and is required to show that he is presently able to operate a motor vehicle. The fact of his having had treatment in a mental hospital is noted on his driving record. This is true for employment records, insurance applications, and applications for military service. By avoiding hospitalization we avoid the label applied to those who are admitted to a mental hospital.

Another benefit of avoiding admission to a mental hospital is that chronicity and social disability is thereby averted. The very fact of hospitalization not only labels the individual but also contributes to his disease process. Hospitalization promotes regression and the final picture after months (perhaps years) of institutional treat- ment is at least as much due to the hospital setting as to the in- trinsic disease process itself. This has been demonstrated repeti- tively (see Introduction). The avoidance of hospitalization is secondary prevention. It means prevention of the disability asso- ciated with hospitalization. It prevents the regressive aspects of the illness from developing for lack of treatment.

To recapitulate, family crisis therapy results in a resolution of the crisis for the individual, a lessening of tension, remission of symp- toms, a recompensation, and avoidance of admission to a mental hospital. In addition, it teaches the individual patient alternative ways of dealing with the subsequent crises of life—it teaches him that there are solutions other than treatment in a mental hospital.

THE FAMILY

What effect does family crisis therapy have on the family? By the time a member of the family is brought to a mental hospital and the doctors decide that he is sick enough to be admitted, the identi- fied patient is not the only member of that family in trouble. By this time the family has been struggling with the crisis and with the patient's symptoms and behavior. They are exhausted and ready to give up. If it is the first admission to a mental hospital, the family have probably tried to avoid it for a while. If the pa- tient has been in a mental hospital before, the family have probably turned to the hospital far earlier. The Jones family is a good ex- ample. The mother, in particular, had been struggling with Portia's regression and catatonic symptoms for two or three weeks before bringing her to the hospital. Although the father had been work- ing, he too was suffering from inadequate rest. Portia's younger brother, who had been away at camp, was going to have to remain in camp until Portia settled down and became less "sexy." In the Carver case, the family had traveled all night to come back from Kansas after Mrs. Carver's suicide attempt in the home of her in-

laws there. As a matter of fact, the trip to Kansas had been initiated because Mrs. Carver had been restless and depressed for
several weeks and Mr. Carver thought it would do his wife some
good to make this visit. In the case of a caretaker crisis such as
the Little case, it is often the caretaker (as well as the family) who
is exhausted and ready to "give up." This description of the situation in the family (or in the caretaker) suggests one effect of family crisis therapy. There is a reduction in tension not only for the
identified patient, but for the entire family. As soon as the crisis
team offers help and says that they will be available around the
clock, the family as well as the patient begin to relax. In the
Jones case it took several days of treatment before Portia abandoned
her psychotic symptom and the family were convinced of her
change. However, the promise of help from the team gave the
family the courage to go on for those few days. This length of
time in the Portia Jones case is reasonably typical of other similar
acute schizophrenic situations. The patient may remain psychotic
for a few days, with a gradual rather than dramatic recompensation
and diminution in the psychotic behavior. The offer of help from
the team plus the medication for the patient and other family members where indicated, will permit all concerned to get a little rest.
Sleep is the best possible tranquilizer. Very often other family
members, in addition to the identified patient, are upset and tense
and unable to get to sleep. One of the first goals of the treatment
is to give everyone some rest. In many cases this means prescribing
a tranquilizer or a sedative for a family member other than the
identified patient. By the next day the state of the family is very
often dramatically altered. They are refreshed and ready to take
up new approaches to the problems. Although one day earlier they
had been exhausted, frustrated and confused, as well as involved
in the crisis, they return the next day with energy for a fresh
approach. The concept of tension at a family level (as opposed to
individual level) is not as familiar to most clinicians as the concept
of tension within a given person. However, the picture of a family
in crisis is different from the picture of that same family in their
usual circumstances. The tension of a family crisis is more than the
sum of the individual pressures. The family in crisis is a disorganized upset group who are not helping one another. As the crisis
gets resolved, the picture of the family as a unit changes.

In the Simpson case the alteration in the family situation was most apparent after the dramatic confrontation of husband and wife. Although Mr. and Mrs. Simpson did not get back to living together for several months, the relationship between them was changed by the one interview. Prior to the interview reported in detail in Chapter 4, they had been enemies. As a result of the interview, the husband and wife, who had been fighting, now became allies against the neighbor. For Mr. Simpson this helped change his behavior. The difference for the husband-wife as a family was the difference between entente and open warfare.

With the reduction of tension, the family acquires a capacity for more efficient problem solving. In the Carver case the solution to the family problem was worked out reasonably rapidly. Mrs. Carver had found the "doll's house" arrangement a reasonable one until her mother encouraged her to change it. For Mrs. Carver to become independent and to have a job outside the home was a real threat to her husband. Once the tension in the Carver family was reduced, the solution to the family problem was that Mrs. Carver would compromise by taking a part time job. Eventually she quit working altogether. In this family the solution was a gentle return to the status quo. The solution to the family problem in the Jones case was gradually worked out after the family upset was diminished. Portia was helped to find a job but was a girl who was sick enough to require more than job placement. She required the help of a rehabilitation program.

Another effect of family crisis therapy is that it gets each family member back to functioning in the tasks he has to carry out in order to keep the family going. This occurs far more rapidly when hospitalization is avoided. For the family breadwinner to be out of work for days, weeks or months is an economic disaster. Someone has to earn the money to pay the bills. In many cases the admission of a breadwinner to a mental hospital means that the extended family must be called in or that the family has to go on welfare. The avoidance of hospitalization permits the family to maintain its functional integrity as a basic social unit; it keeps the family off the relief rolls; it keeps all members of the affected family living together.

Another result is not easy to quantify. That factor is the shame and guilt which a family experiences when they hospitalize one of the family members. In most instances the fact of hospitalization is viewed by the family as a failure—a failure to solve a problem on its own. From another point of view, the family are ashamed that friends, neighbors and other members of the community will know about the problem. All families hide the fact that an aunt or a grandmother or an adolescent child is a "mental hospital case." Despite our enlightened "acceptance" of mental illness and of psychiatric treatment, there is still a great deal of stigma associated with the label.

In summary, the effect of crisis treatment on the family is to reduce the symptoms of acute upset within the family itself and to free up the family's problem solving capacities. The family as a unit is returned to its previous operations and its previous levels of functioning. The deleterious effects of hospitalizing a family member including the economic stresses and the shame and guilt are avoided by using family crisis therapy as an alternative to hospitalization.

THE COMMUNITY

Not only is the individual patient and his family affected by mental illness, but to the community in which he lives, it is also a problem. The citizen who is not able to work because of a crisis contributes little. If his crisis results in a serious illness and the need for mental hospital treatment, it constitutes an additional disaster. Mental illness and its treatment have been a costly drain on community resources. Even when the treatment is custodial (and thereby erroneously presumed to be less costly) it is expensive. For centuries our communities and governments have recognized that the cost of managing a chronic mental illness is so great that it cannot be assumed by the individual or his family. State supported mental hospitals were established for this specific reason. The cost of caring for or even treating mental illness was a burden which the local community with its limited tax base could not manage. The cost of mental illness has been borne by the state and federal government. In addition to the cost of the services, there are additional costs in terms of tax revenues lost because people are out of work. There are the costs of providing homemakers, when it is the mother who is hospitalized. There are the costs of lack of productivity when the patient is released from the hospital. Long-term hospitalization often promotes or enhances social disability. Mental illness is expensive in those areas where its cost can be measured. In the areas where measurements are more difficult, such as the suffering of the families, we can only guess at the extent of the expense.

For this reason it has been deemed worthwhile to calculate the comparative costs of hospital treatment and of family crisis therapy. If family crisis treatment can be shown to keep people out of mental hospitals and save money and yet accomplish results not dissimilar from the hospital treatment program, it would be a worthwhile demonstration indeed.

In this project we have demonstrated clearly that family crisis treatment keeps "patients" out of mental hospitals. The comparisons of social functioning, of adaptation, and of management of subsequent crises which will be eventually measured for both experimentals and controls have been described in Chapter 8. However, these data are not yet available on a large enough group for statistically significant conclusions. The final report of the project will present this in detail.

It would not be reasonable to say that the costs of this demonstration project are representative of what the costs of treatment would be on a service basis in a community mental health center. The project has had the task of developing a treatment approach in a pioneer area. Although the general principals of crisis treatment are not new, we know of no other group which has regularly used crisis treatment on a conjoint family basis with a population which would ordinarily be immediately hospitalized. For this reason the project proceeded slowly. In addition, the personnel of the project were charged with obtaining control cases and the measurements of effectiveness on control, as well as experimental cases. The professionals of the project team have also been engaged in teaching these technics to other mental health workers.

We do know, however, the estimated cost of a clinical team consisting of a psychiatrist, a clinical psychologist, a psychiatric social worker, a psychiatric-public health nurse and two clerical personnel. Using salary scales presently in effect for this general area and which are considered competitive with other metropolitan areas, the annual budget for salaries of this team would be approximately

$65,000. Supplies, overhead and a small amount of money for professional travel might consume another $5,000 per year. Thus we would see the operational budget for such a team as being on the order of $70,000 per year.

The clinical personnel of our project have discussed at various times the number of new cases per week which could be undertaken by a clinical team as outlined above. These estimates have ranged from five new cases per week to ten new cases per week. In our own experience the random selection procedures have given us from one to seven new cases per week at various times through the history of the project. If we assume conservatively that such a crisis team could manage seven new cases per week, or approximately 350 new cases per year, the acute crisis treatment can be carried on at a cost of approximately $200 per case.

Compare this with the cost of mental hospital treatment; The control cases were treated in a university psychiatric hospital whose costs are quite similar to those of other modern treatment centers. The cost of hospital treatment at the Colorado Psychiatric Hospital is almost $50.00 per day. This does not include the salaries of psychiatric residents and staff psychiatrists who are paid by teaching budgets. Patients treated in Colorado Psychiatric Hospital have an average stay of approximately twenty-six days. To treat a patient in the hospital for twenty-six days at $50.00 a day means a cost of $1300 per case. The comparison is impressive! $1300 per treated case as opposed to $200 per treated case! Certainly one might question certain aspects of these estimates. Perhaps a team could average only six cases a week instead of seven; perhaps the budget might be a bit higher. But there is no question about the differences in cost between outpatient crisis treatment and inpatient hospital treatment. The factors are on the order of a six time difference.

What are the results of family crisis therapy? For the individual the results are a resolution of the crisis and a return to functioning, an avoidance of admission to a mental hospital and perhaps new ways of resolving serious crises. For the family it means a resolution of the family crisis and a return to functioning as a family unit. It means an avoidance of breaking up the family by hospitalizing one member, and of the economic and emotional disasters associated with mental hospitalization. For the community it means that "patients" can be treated at far less cost, can continue as functional and contributing members of the society in which they live, and that the productivity of many community human resources can be conserved.

In summary, the operation and techniques of the Family Treatment Unit has demonstrated the following results:

(1) All of the first 75 experimental cases, a random sample of patients admitted to Colorado Psychiatric Hospital who live in a family and who live in the metropolitan area, could be treated by family crisis therapy. Hospitalization was avoided in all 75 cases.

(2) Even though long-standing problems may not be resolved, rapid recompensation of acute psychosis is possible with these technics.

(3) The treatment does not merely postpone hospitalization. It avoids admission. When hospitalization takes place subsequently, it is briefer.

(4) There is no evidence that patients treated outside the hospital are more likely to commit suicide or homicide or are more chronically disabled than patients treated in a hospital.

(5) Though the family may have certain burdens added as a result of home treatment, many advantages accrue, especially increased awareness of crises, new technics for handling them, clarification and perhaps resolution of dissatisfactions of other family members, greater family cohesiveness and a heightened sense of the family's competence to manage its own problems.

(6) The well known stigmata of mental hospitalization are avoided as are the tendencies toward chronicity and social disability.

(7) The symptomatic members return more rapidly to usual role functioning within the family.

(8) The cost of family crisis therapy is less than one sixth the cost of mental hospital treatment. These figures are the direct costs and do not consider the expense of diminished productivity and of human suffering.

CHAPTER 10

Implications

What are the implications of using family crisis therapy for hospitalizable patients? The innovator is responsible for setting his
findings into place. Having demonstrated that family crisis therapy
will keep people out of mental hospitals, we face the same responsibility. As we have outlined in Chapter 8, our comparative evaluation will give us systematic data on the full sample within a year or
two. Assuming that the data demonstrates that family crisis therapy
not only keeps patients out of mental hospitals but also keeps them
functioning in the community, where does it fit into the scheme of
available mental health services? We can tentatively make that
assumption out of the evidence of our clinical experience and out
of preliminary analyses of data.[2]

Is family crisis therapy a new treatment? The basic principles
behind it are not. Similar technics have undoubtedly been used
before for isolated cases. Any clinician can cite occasional cases
from his practice in which hospitalization has been avoided by his
intensive crisis oriented efforts—usually with the individual, sometimes with the family. It is increasingly fashionable to see whole
families together so the conjoint family approach can hardly be the
contribution of the project we report. Those who have done crisis
therapy in emergency room settings or in walk-in clinics will not
be surprised at the results reported because they have also been
keeping potentially hospitalizable patients functioning in the community. It is no longer new to consider mental illness a product of
family interaction. But no one has systematically used family crisis
therapy as an alternative to mental hospitalization. No one has
systematically compared the results of each of these treatments in
similar populations. No one has reported a systematic follow-up of
the results of each of these types of treatment.

The enthusiast might be tempted to say that we can close down
most mental hospitals. However, a certain proportion of our cases

treated by family crisis therapy have been admitted to a mental hospital after crisis treatment. There will always be need for *some* psychiatric beds though at this point it is difficult to predict how many. Another factor overlooked by those who would close all mental hospitals is the fact that the patients treated by us all live in families. Some families are very helpful in times of trouble. Others are destructive, but our impression has been that with a little bit of help, a family can exert a strong influence towards health. We have no idea how well this family crisis treatment would work for people who do not live in a family, because we haven't tested it. Although we can obtain clinical impressions from our colleagues who do crisis therapy with those patients who do not live in a family, we cannot compare their results with ours. The populations are different; it is unfortunate that we recognized this deficiency in our evaluation study after it was too late to do something about it. Perhaps some other group will systematically compare the results of outpatient crisis treatment and mental hospital treatment for those who do not live with a family. Because 30 per cent of the usual population of Colorado Psychiatric Hospital does not live in a family, we have no firm data on how well they would fare without the mental hospital. For this reason the mental hospital is likely to be with us for a while although we hope that fewer people will require admission.

We do not think that family crisis therapy will replace *all* existing treatments, but the results suggest that it should be an important addition. The point of view that family crisis therapy is a remedy for all forms of mental illness and emotional struggles will not be advanced by the serious professional. The medicine man who sold remedies for falling hair, rheumatism, cancer, impotence, and "anything that ails you" was generally a good enough showman to create interest. However, his product did not stand the test of time. Family crisis therapy will obviously not "cure everything that ails you." The evaluative study and the clinical experience of those who have used this approach in treatment do suggest, however, that it is very helpful in recompensating acutely ill patients and disturbed families.

Though we lack all the data at this time, we will attempt to offer some views on the following questions:

1. What are the implications of family crisis therapy for theory? How do the results of family crisis therapy throw light on explanations of human behavior? What do the findings contribute to the theories of treatment?

2. What have been the effects of the Family Treatment Unit on the other clinical psychiatric divisions of the University of Colorado Medical Center? Has the operation of the Family Treatment Unit changed the local scene?

3. What are the implications of family crisis therapy for seriously ill patients? Should all mental health centers use family crisis therapy as an alternative to mental hospital admission?

4. Who can do family crisis therapy? Should it be carried on by a specialized team who do nothing else? Is this a skill which should be taught to one or more mental health professions? What specific disciplines can treat hospitalizable patients using this approach?

IMPLICATIONS FOR THEORY

Family crisis therapy suggests that families are important in creating crises and in treating them. The implication for theory is that those who investigate crises should look at the family setting in which they arise. The behavior of the individual will be influenced by those with whom he is interacting as well as by his psychology and biology. These three areas of influence on human behavior must be kept in appropriate theoretical perspective, but until recent years, the family had been neglected by psychiatry. Our work would support the implications that crises are important in producing the symptoms of mental illness and that crises are related to immediate settings and current events. The kinds of family factors which contribute to the intensity of a crisis, can be reversed to calm and resolve the crisis. The repetitive demonstrations of improvement in regressive symptoms by diminishing the tension in a family lends conviction to the importance of social factors in mental illness. Only systematic research can partial out the influences of the family as well as the contributions of biology and psychology, but none of the three can be neglected.

Another area of interest for theory is the "normal" crisis. Our clinical work has been with very sick individuals and very troubled families. All the patients were judged in need of immediate mental hospitalization. We have, therefore, seen only certain kinds of families and only certain kinds of crises. Our model of a crisis concerns itself with: (1) the stress event or hazard; and (2) the reaction of the individual and the family. The hazards which have precipitated a serious crisis in our families are events which other families master with ease. If the same problem is mastered without a serious crisis in one family and precipitates a psychotic reaction within another, we have a natural experiment which may help partial out the effect of family forces (interaction) and the individual's susceptibility.

Even in those families in which the stress was sudden, unexpected and serious, there were long-term patterns of poor functioning. Our case material would not support a "bolt from the blue" concept which overemphasizes the stressor event and underemphasizes the family in which the bolt strikes. It takes more than a hazard to produce a crisis and more than a crisis to produce a psychotic regression. More attention needs to be devoted to the way in which "normal" individuals and familes deal with specific crises. This would improve our understanding of the differential effects of the stress on the one hand, and the health and stability of the family and its members on the other.

EFFECTS ON CLINICAL PRACTICE

What effect has the family crisis therapy team had on the clinical setting in which the work was done? The Family Treatment Unit has had a significant and visible influence on clinical operations in other divisions. The Family Treatment Unit is a part of the Colorado Psychiatric Hospital. The Director of the Family Treatment Unit (DGL) is also Director of Inpatient Service. The FTU Co-Director (DMK) was Director of Psychiatric Social Work for the Department of Psychiatry from the inception of the project until he left Denver in July 1967. The Department of Psychiatry at the University of Colorado Medical Center has been well known throughout the country for its excellent clinical training programs in psychiatry, psychology and the other mental health professions. The orientation of the department has been traditionally "psychoanalytic." That label means that most of the senior members of the Department are psychoanalysts and that the department itself is committed basically to an individual psychotherapy orientation. It does not mean that the department is unwilling to use and teach other treatment technics and other points of view—obviously! Though the senior author and director of this project (DGL) is a psychoanalyst, only part of his working day is spent in traditional psychoanalytic practice. This is true of the other clinical division heads in the Department of Psychiatry. The clinical divisions include an Adult Psychiatric Outpatient Clinic (generally oriented towards longer term, one to one psychotherapy), a Child Psychiatry Division (with a heavy orientation towards the use of teams, and an interest in families, though also very much committed to individual psychotherapy, the Emergency Psychiatric Service (interested in individual crisis therapy), and a Psychiatric Liaison Division (specializing in consultation in the General Hospital). The Adult Inpatient Service is a 78 bed hospital (Colorado Psychiatric Hospital) which has been committed to brief hospitalization, the recompensation of the acutely mentally ill, a team operation, and emphasis on therapeutic milieu.

The description of the clinical divisions in the Department is offered to give the reader some picture of the setting in which this research was done. How much the effects on clinical operations had to do with the fact that the Director and Co-Director of the Family Project were also senior members of the department can only be a matter of conjecture. We would prefer to think that the clinical effectiveness of the operation, rather than the administrative titles of its directors, have been the forces which motivated the change. And there has been change! The dramatic change is the popularity and success of individual crisis treatment on the Emergency Psychiatric Service. That unit used to be an evaluation center to decide whether or not a patient would be admitted to the mental hospital or sent home.[1] Since its inception it has been able to reduce the proportion of patients seen and admitted to the Psychiatric Hospital from 52 per cent to 26 per cent. The success of the family crisis therapy in keeping people out of hospitals began to be known after the first year or two of the clinical operation started in June 1964. As a result of the local knowledge of the efficacy of this treatment, residents and staff on the Emergency Psychiatric Service began to see families conjointly. This was not their exclusive treatment approach, but rather one that was added to their already existing method of individual crisis therapy.

In addition to the success in keeping people out of the hospital, another factor which led to a change in practice was the clinical teaching offered by Family Treatment Unit personnel. The fulltime psychiatrist on the project (FSP) taught a large number of psychiatric residents; the nurse (CDY) taught undergraduate and graduate nursing students; the psychologist (PM) taught a seminar and supervised the individual work of clinical psychology students at the intern and post-doctoral level; the psychiatric social worker (KF) contributed to the teaching of graduate students in his own field. Thus the combination of clinical success, a great deal of teaching by the clinicians of the project, and the role models offered by the administrators resulted in a great increase in interest in family psychology and in clinical work with families. As a result of this stimulation, Inpatient Service personnel are now more prone to work directly with families through collaborative therapy; in some cases they do conjoint family therapy with inpatients. On the Child Psychiatry Division, there has been more interest in work with families. Regular seminars and meetings have been devoted to the discussion of clinical family therapy. A great increase of interest in family therapy has been felt throughout the clinical divisions of the department and has obviously had an impact on clinical practice. Truly this project, which was funded as a "demonstration project," has been a clinical demonstration and has had a significant effect on local clinical practice. From the number of inquiries from other mental health centers and from conversations at national meetings, it is safe to assume that the project has had certain influences on clinical practice in other areas.

IMPLICATIONS FOR ORGANIZING MENTAL HEALTH SERVICES

The implications for organizing mental health services are relatively straightforward. Family crisis therapy ought to be available as an alternative to committing patients to a mental hospital. The hospitalization of an acutely disturbed member of a family has been shown to have profound effects on the identified patient, on the family and on the course of the illness (see Introduction). In addition it is a very expensive form of treatment (see Chapter 9). If another form of treatment for the same patient will keep him out of the hospital at far less expense to himself (psychologically and economically), to his family and to the community, that treatment should be tried. If the experience of the Family Treatment Unit is replicable, it should be able to keep a large majority of patients out of the mental hospital. If the crisis service continues to be available at times of future crises, the success in keeping the patient out of the hospital should continue. As an approach to the resolution of acute problems and crises, family crisis therapy is certainly effective. There is a temptation, of course, to focus so heavily on this one approach that other treatments are not made available.

The sad fact is that mental health professionals in the past have had only two options—either admission to a state mental hospital or return home without treatment. A few patients were able to afford private psychiatric treatment in hospitals or offices, but these were a small minority. In the past the patient has been made to fit the treatment or the institution rather than receiving treatment designed to meet his needs. Since the community psychiatry approach has been developed, and since the organization of the comprehensive community mental health centers, some attempts have been made to correct this deficiency. It is hoped that the comprehensive community mental health center which provides at least the five basic services (twenty-four hour emergency services, partial hospitalization, twenty-four hour hospitalization, outpatient services and consultation services) will take steps to fit the treatment to the patients needs. In any event, the numbers of options have increased.

Family crisis therapy should be *one of many* treatment approaches. It can be an effective alternative to mental hospitalization. Short-term crisis therapy—either individual or family oriented —will not accomplish changes in long-term behavioral patterns. It will not cure an illness or behavior which has been in existence for years. It does not offer the insight into unconscious conflicts that we are accustomed to seeing in long-term psychotherapy or psychoanalysis. It obviously is not a treatment which can be carried on at a family level when the individual has no family. It will not prevent *all* hospitalizations and a certain proportion of patients will doubtless come to be admitted to a mental hospital no matter how widely available family crisis therapy happens to be.

Family crisis therapy is not easy to do and is extremely demanding of the treatment team. It requires certain skills which will not be a part of the equipment of each and every mental health professional. It also requires twenty-four hour coverage. We are firmly convinced by the model of the family physician that rapid availability of help and the other nonspecific factors in the treatment process are exceedingly important. A family crisis team will of necessity be limited in its size and, therefore, will not be able to have someone from a three or four person team constantly available on twenty-four hour call. Even a crisis team needs the backup help of its colleagues to share night and weekend call. For this reason, all professionals in a mental health clinic should know something about this treatment because they will have to participate in the call schedule.

In summary, the implications as we see them for organizing mental health services for citizens of this country, are that family crisis therapy should be made available for the treatment of such crises as precipitate a psychotic regression and which might result in a mental hospital admission. Once the crisis has resolved, other treatment may be advisable, especially for long-term illness or chronic disturbances. The family crisis therapy should be one of a number of treatment modalities available.

WHO CAN PRACTICE FAMILY CRISIS THERAPY?

In Chapter 3 we pointed out that some aspects of family crisis therapy could be carried on by any of the traditional mental health professionals—psychiatrists, psychologists, social workers and nurses. We also pointed out that certain functions were specialized as well as generalized, and we tried to indicate the value of a team doing this kind of treatment. There have been very real advantages in the team operation. Although innovation and experimentation should certainly be encouraged, we think that the team approach to family crisis therapy will probably continue.

There are a number of experiments going on to train people to work with the populations which require mental health services. In some areas indigenous nonprofessionals, with minimal education and brief periods of training, have been extremely useful, especially among disadvantaged groups. There have been many indications that the immediate support and understanding offered by these individuals has been of value in keeping decompensation from proceeding. Other experiments have been conducted with housewives whose children are now grown. They have been taught to do individual psychotherapy. A new profession is in the course of being developed—the profession of the "mental health worker." This group will have the equivalent of two years of training and again individuals from this area could well be incorporated into a crisis team.

There has been extensive interest in crisis treatment and in brief treatment by all of the traditional mental health professions. The professions whose training requires at least a master's level of preparation (all four basic mental health professions) have all shown interest in family crisis therapy. With the movement towards making mental health services available to all by way of the comprehensive community mental health center, these professions will broaden their roles and skills and operate from the mental health center base. The groups who have not worked out clear roles in the community mental health center are the less extensively trained workers. They have been variously labeled "nonprofessionals" or "subprofessionals." They include the experimental groups listed above and the psychiatric aides, attendants, or "technicians." These groups have been predominantly hospital based and have been closely supervised (in the well staffed mental hospitals). The outpatient operation of the mental health center is one where less supervision is available. In the hospital there are many opportunities to pick up errors in practice or in treatment because there are highly trained people available around the clock. The patient is under observation and is "protected." While we do not agree with the usual rationalizations that such protection is necessary or that so much supervision is necessary, practitioners will have to be aware of the dangers of untrained therapists doing outpatient treatment when supervision is inadequate.

There are implications for change in training programs in all mental health professions. The psychiatrist comes into his residency with the medical model; some experience in the approach of the family doctor is available to him. He learns to put it aside when he

is doing insight oriented psychotherapy and becomes more of a
passive listener than an active doer. However, with the encouragement that would be afforded by making family crisis therapy an
accepted part of the training program in a psychiatric residency,
the resident would quickly learn such skills. At this center, where
psychiatric residents have become accustomed to working on the
Emergency Psychiatric Service (during their third year of training)
for a three or four month block of time, they have enthusiastically
and skilfully learned to do individually oriented crisis therapy. They
have also become increasingly interested in doing family crisis
therapy. More residents are seeing whole families in crisis treatment during their tour on the Emergency Psychiatric Service. During the most recent academic year three psychiatric residents have
elected to be assigned to the Family Treatment Unit for clinical
training and experience.

Clinical psychologists, psychiatric nurses (those with public
health experience work out very well) and psychiatric social
workers will all be learning to do crisis therapy in increasing numbers. One of the major implications of family crisis therapy and
individual crisis therapy has to do with changing patterns of professional education to include individual and family oriented crisis
therapy as part of the basic training. The requirement that a community mental health center provide twenty-four hour emergency
psychiatric services in order to qualify for federal construction or
staffing aid, will make it even more apparent to those who train
mental health professionals, that crisis therapy clinical experience is
a necessary part of professional education.

SUMMARY

Family crisis therapy calls on previously known models of crisis
therapy and of knowledge about families. The clinical experience
of the Family Treatment Unit has organized a package of mental
health services, taking leads from knowledge about individual crisis
and its treatment, from family psychology, and from our knowledge
of the recompensation of seriously ill patients. The other contribution has to do with the systematic evaluation of the effects of this
treatment. Although no one else has worked systematically with a
population which would ordinarily be admitted to a mental hos-

pital, and has kept this population out of the hospital, we feel that more is needed than anecdotal claims of success. Scientific evaluation is absolutely necessary. There is a tragic dearth of such systematic evaluation in psychiatry. There have been reasons why more adequate evaluation has not been done. It is difficult to control for all of the complex variables which contribute to human behavior. It takes a great deal of energy and financial support to keep track of a large group of cases. It is important to choose an experimental and a control population in a manner such that results can be generalized. It takes real dedication on the part of clinicians because they do not value research as highly as clinical practice. Nonetheless this project demonstrates that all of these conditions can be overcome. As this clinical report is written, the collection of data for evaluation of the results of treatment is going on. We close this book with a promise that these data will be carefully analyzed and will be published. The initial results are extremely encouraging. We have presented only a sample of the kinds of data which will eventually be available. It is very worthwhile to keep people out of mental hospitals—it is especially worthwhile to show that they can do as well by avoiding the hospital as if they had been admitted.

Bibliography

1. Kritzer, H. and Langsley, D. G. Training for emergency psychiatric services. J. Med. Educ. 42:1111-1115, 1967.

2. Langsley, D G., Pittman, F S., Machotka, P. and Flomenhaft, K. Family crisis therapy: Results and implications. Family Process, in press.

Index